Timesaver Pronunciation Activities

(Elementary - Intermediate)

Bill Bowler

Contents

Introduction

Section 1 - Pronunciation Puzzles

Section 2 - Fun with Phonetics

Section 3 - Speak Out

Section 4 - Listen In

Section 5 - Linking and Accents

Introduction

About *Timesaver Pronunciation Activities*

The photocopiable materials in this book are designed to be used in secondary school classes with students of elementary to intermediate levels – levels and timings are shown at the top of the page. The materials provide self-contained pronunciation lessons (and parts of lessons) with teen appeal that teachers can use to supplement their ordinary general English coursebook, where good pronunciation tasks are often lacking.

The activities in this book are divided into five categories:

1 Pronunciation Puzzles

These puzzle activities involve sorting, matching and sentence completion tasks. They focus on sounding the alphabet, word stress patterns and schwa, grammar-related pronunciation (-*ed* past endings, -*ed* adjective endings, 3rd person singular present simple -*s* endings, plural -*s* endings), rhyming words, sound-alike words (homophones), and silent letters. Working through the tasks in this section, students engage cognitively with the patterns of English pronunciation. Simple pronunciation rules are provided where appropriate in the key as a follow up – to consolidate students' understanding of sound and stress patterns that they have grasped inductively.

2 Fun with Phonetics

These concrete task-based activities break down the 44 English phonetic symbols into a number of convenient teaching blocks: long vowels, short vowels, easy to recognise voiceless consonants, easy to recognise voiced consonants, double vowel sounds (diphthongs) and hard to recognise consonants. Activities in this section are designed to be used together with Bill Bowler's Phonetic Colour Chart. Further exploitation activities are given in the *Teaching the chart* and *Games and activities to use with the chart* sections. A photocopiable version of the chart for students to colour and personalise with their own example words appears on page 8 of this book.

3 Speak Out

These activities focus on productive pronunciation. They involve students

actively in using standard British English pronunciation to bridge an information gap. There is a focus on sounds which are problematic for speakers of a number of languages including French, German, Greek, Italian, Polish and Spanish, though many other nationalities will also benefit.

Activities in this section begin with minimal pair and triplet work – listening, and controlled recognition and production. This leads into a freer information gap task, which includes map-marking, grid filling, or dictation as an outcome. The successful completion of these final tasks is dependent on correct production and reception of problematic sounds. After completion of the task, students are asked to reflect on the effectiveness of their communication.

The activity focus and suggested suitability for use by students of different nationalities is shown in the table below.

Worksheets 2-9 can easily be adapted for use with other sound contrasts that your students may have problems with. Some suggestions are given below, but you may choose words to practise other sounds.

Worksheet 2: no changes are required to the Shape Dictation Grid page in order to change the sound focus. Other minimal pairs to use here – suitable for German, Greek and Polish speakers – are: cap/cab, nip/nib, pup/pub, rip/rib, slap/slab (focusing on final /p/ and /b/).

Worksheet 3: blank out with correction fluid the sound symbols on the Sound Bingo Card page and write in new sound symbols in order to change the sound focus. Other minimal pairs to use here – suitable for German, Greek and

Polish speakers – are: calf/carve, half/halve, leaf/leave, life/live (adj), proof/proove, safe/save, thief/thieve (focusing on final /f/ and /v/).

Worksheet 4: blank out with correction fluid the example words on the Edit the Words Grid page and write in new words in order to change the sound focus. Other minimal pairs to use here – suitable for German, Greek and Polish speakers – are: back/bag, clock/clog, bucks/bugs, dock/dog, lock/log, pick/pig, rack/rag, sack/sag. (focusing on final /k/ and /g/).

Worksheet 5: no changes are required to the Picasso's Paints page in order in order to change the sound focus. (You must however choose words that students can draw easily, or give them simple pictures to copy.) Other minimal triplets to use here – suitable for French, German, Greek, Italian, Polish and Spanish speakers – are: bed/bad/bud, beg/bag/bug, hem/ham/hum, ten/tan/ton (focusing on /e/ /æ/ and /ʌ/).

Worksheet 6: blank out with correction fluid the street names on the Street Map of Letterton page and write in new street names to change the sound focus. Other minimal pairs to use here – suitable for French speakers – are: bud/bird, bun/burn, fun/fern, gull/girl, shut/shirt/, ton/turn (focusing on /ʌ/ and /ɜː/).

Worksheet 7: blank out with correction fluid the example words on the vertical axis of the Find Pharaoh's jewels grid page and write in new words focusing on other minimal triplets instead. Other minimal triplets to use here – suitable for Greek and Italian speakers – are: pen/pain/pine, letter/later/lighter, pepper/paper/piper, tell/tail/tile, wet/wait/white (focusing on /e/ /eɪ/ and /aɪ/).

Worksheet	Focus	Suitable for speakers of:
1 (p.45)	mouth & tongue position	all languages
2 (p.46-47)	/ɪ/ and /iː/	French, Italian, Polish, Spanish, etc.
3 (p.48-49)	/uː/ and /ʊ/	French, Greek, Italian, Polish, Spanish, etc.
4 (p.50-52)	/e/ and /eɪ/	French, Greek, Italian, Polish, Spanish, etc.
5 (p.53-54)	/æ/ /ʌ/ and /ɑː/	French, Greek, Italian, Spanish, etc.
6 (p.55-56)	/v/ and /w/	German, Polish, etc.
7 (p.57-59)	/n/ /ŋ/ and /ŋk/	French, German, Italian, Polish, Spanish, etc.
8 (p.60-62)	/h/	French, Italian, Spanish, etc.
9 (p.63-65)	/j/ /dʒ/ and /tʃ/	German, Italian, Spanish, etc.
10 (p.66-67)	/d/ /ð/ /z/ and /t/ /θ/ /s/	French, German, Italian, Polish, Spanish, etc.

Worksheet 8: no changes are required to the Monster Maze page in order to change the sound focus. Other minimal pairs to use here – suitable for German, Greek and Polish speakers – are: bat/bad, bought/bored, cart/card, let/led, seats/seeds, write/ride (focusing on final /t/ and /d/).

Worksheet 9: blank out with correction fluid the example words on the vertical axis of the Map of Elf Palace page and write in new words to change the sound focus. Other minimal triplets to use here – suitable for French, German, Greek, Italian, Polish and Spanish speakers – are: cock/cork/Coke, cod/cord/code, fox/forks/folks, shone/shorn/shown, wok/walk/woke (focusing on /ɑ/ /ɔ:/ and /əʊ/).

NOTE A standard British English accent is modelled in these activities as it is less confusing for students to have one clear model to follow. Realistically most students will aspire to this model rather than absolutely master it. These activities set the standard high in order to make students aware in class of their latent problems and to help them reduce misunderstanding and move towards a neutral standard pronunciation which will allow greater communicative transparency with other L2 speakers of English.

4 Listen In
These activities focus on developing receptive understanding of stress and intonation.

Stress activities include shifting word stress (in -ty and -teen words and noun/verb homographs), strong and weak forms, schwa at sentence level, sentence stress and rhythm, and corrective stress. Intonation activities include intonation in lists, statements, yes/no and Wh- questions, question tags, and intonation and stress in polite requests. Fun practice activities are provided as a final outcome.

5 Linking and Accents
This section makes students aware of contractions and linking used by native speakers in normal-speed speech. It also exposes students in a controlled way to a variety of different accents in English (Australian, American, Cockney and Jamaican.) The main aim here is to

provide ear-training – making different English accents more accessible, and less alien to students' ears. Another aim is to raise students' awareness that not all English speakers they will meet in the real world speak the Standard English frequent in many English Language Teaching materials. Students are not advised permanently to adopt these accents. Instead they are encouraged to recognise them through their key features, and to imitate them playfully.

Teaching the chart

1 The chart is designed so that you can write in an example word above each symbol on it, underlining the letters in the word that correspond to the sound of the symbol. These words act as 'memory keys' for the sounds.

Possible example words for the symbols are the following, though of course you can choose your own:

Voiceless consonants (green)
/h/ hi
/p/ please
/t/ ten
/k/ key
/f/ fat
/s/ see

Voiced consonants (blue)
/b/ book
/d/ dog
/g/ good
/v/ very
/z/ zebra
/l/ like
/r/ run
/w/ Walkman
/m/ mother
/n/ nice

Long vowels (yellow)
/i:/ me
/ɜ:/ girl
/ɑ:/ car
/ɔ:/ door
/u:/ cool

Short vowels (pink)
/æ/ cat
/e/ when
/ɪ/ hit
/ə/ again
/ʌ/ up
/ɒ/ not
/ʊ/ good

Alien-looking symbols (green and blue)
/θ/ think
/ʃ/ she
/tʃ/ cheap
/ð/ this
/ʒ/ revision
/dʒ/ January
/ŋ/ bring
/j/ your

Diphthongs (orange)
/eɪ/ day
/aɪ/ my
/ɔɪ/ boy
/əʊ/ now
/aʊ/ no
/ɪə/ here
/eə/ there
/ʊə/ tour

2 Rather than you yourself choosing 'memory key' words for the symbols, it can be very motivating to invite your students as a class to choose their own example words to remember the sounds by.

3 Do not try to teach the whole phonetic chart in one lesson. This will be too time-consuming and too much for students to take in at one go. Instead, to start with at elementary level, focus only on pairs or trios of sounds as they appear in the activities in this book, filling in example words on the chart to help you keep track of the symbols students have met already.

4 To teach a symbol from the chart, point to it, make the sound in isolation – i.e. /ʃ/ rather than /ʃə/ – and get students to repeat. Tell students to look at your lips, tongue and jaw as you make the sound, in order to get the mouth position correct. (You can use Andy the Pronunciation Android page 45 to teach basic vocabulary for talking about mouth position.) Ask students to suggest an example word to help them remember the sound by, and write it on the chart.

5 With long vowels, tell students that the two dots are 'chewing gum'. Ask them to stretch the sounds for as long as possible, accompanying the sounds with stretching movements of the hands as if stretching out chewing gum. With /i:/ both hands should stretch the imaginary gum from the sides of the smiling mouth out to the side. With /ɜ:/ /ɑ:/ /ɔ:/ and /u:/ one hand should stretch the imaginary gum from the open mouth out to the front.

6 With diphthongs, tell students to hold the first symbol of the diphthong in their imagination in their left hand. Tell them to hold the second symbol of the diphthong in their imagination in their right hand. First ask them to turn to the left and make the first sound then turn to the right and make the second sound. Model this and get students to do it with you. Next ask students to turn to the left and make the first sound and then slide into the second sound as they turn their head to the right. Model this and get students to do it with you. (This is a continuation of the Phonetic hang-gliding activity on page 36.) If you wish, students can hold up actual cards in their hands with the diphthong symbols split into first symbol and second symbol written on them, rather than simply imagining the symbols.

7 With continuing consonants – /ʃ/ /ʒ/ /s/ /z/ /f/ /v/ /l/ /r/ /m/ /ŋ/ ask students to continue the sounds for as long as they have breath. You can give a 'Harry Houdini breath control prize' for the student who can keep going with one sound the longest. (Houdini was a famous Hungarian American escape artist of the 1920s who could stay under water for long periods of time because he had very good breath control.) /ʃ/ is a sound British people make to say 'be quiet'. /mmm/ is a sound British people make to say 'delicious'. /mm/ is a sound British people make to say 'yes'/'I agree'. /mm/ /mm/ is a repeated sound British people make to say 'no'.

8 With exploding consonants – /p/ /b/ /t/ /d/ /k/ /g/ /tʃ/ /dʒ/ – ask students to make the sounds singly but repeatedly. /tʃ/ /tʃ/ /tʃ/ is the sound of a train. /dʒ/ /dʒ/ /dʒ/ is the sound people make when they tickle a baby's chin. (You can get students to make appropriate gestures to remind them of these sounds.)

9 With voiceless consonants – /h/ /p/ /t/ /k/ /tʃ/ – ask students to hold up a piece of paper in front of their mouths as they make the sounds. The paper should move a lot as the air rushes out while they make the sounds. (This extra puff of air, or 'aspiration' is especially strong with these sounds in English.) Ask the students to make the voiced consonants /b/ /d/ /g/ /dʒ/ also holding up a piece of paper in front of their

mouths as they make the sounds. The paper should move a lot less.

10 With voiced and voiceless pairs of consonants – /p/ and /b/, /t/ and /d/, /k/ and /g/, /f/ and /v/, /s/ and /z/, /ʃ/ and /ʒ/, and /tʃ/ and /dʒ/ – ask students to put a hand on their voicebox to feel the difference, With the voiced consonants they should feel their voicebox vibrate as they make the sounds. With the voiceless consonants they should not feel their voicebox vibrate as they make the sounds.

11 If you wish, teach the blocks of symbols in the chart, as suggested above, over a number of lessons. Follow the order as suggested in the Fun with Phonetics activities. (There are built-in revision activities – long and short vowels, voiced and voiceless consonants – phonetic hang-gliding – which help to consolidate students' memorisation of the symbols.)

12 It is helpful if each student gets a small photocopy of the colour chart (page 8) to keep as their own personal pronunciation reference tool. Get your students to use crayons or highlighter pens to colour in the different symbol blocks and corresponding key on their photocopies, following the colour scheme on the poster itself – as outlined on page 5. The bright colours are designed to make the chart more memorable and – together with the layout of the symbols in their blocks – help to clarify the differences, the links, and the relationships between the different symbol groups.

Games and activities to use with the chart

1 Phonetic bingo
Give out extra black and white photocopies of the phonetic chart and ask students to focus on one of the blocks of symbols that you have taught. Ask them to cross out half of the symbols in that block randomly. Now say a list of words that contain the sounds in that block one by one. Write up the words one by one on the board, or hold up word cards one by one as you do so. After listening to each word, students write it down above the appropriate uncrossed symbol on their chart. The student who first fills the spaces above all

their uncrossed symbols in the block shouts 'Bingo'. If all their words are correctly placed on the chart, that student is the winner.

2 Sticky word race
Ask students to choose their favourite word from a reading text or a vocabulary set, write it on a sticky notelet, and underline one of the sounds in the word. When you say 'Go', each student must run and stick his or her notelet in the correct place on the phonetic poster, according to the underlined sound in the word. The first student to put their word in the correct place is the winner.

3 Sticky word pile-up
Put students in groups and give each group a different symbol on the chart. Give each group some sticky notelets and ask one student from each group to be the runner. When you say 'Go' the students in each group should write an example word on each notelet for their sound, taking care to underline the letters that represent the sound. The runner from each group should take the notelets one by one, run up to the chart, and stick them in the correct place, one on top of the other, running back to collect a new notelet each time. After an agreed time limit, stop the game. The group with the most correct example words stuck on the chart is the winner.

4 Listen and point
Ask students to listen to a list of words one by one. After each word students should hold up their phonetic chart and point to the correct vowel sound in the word. (This technique can also be used to focus on the consonant sound at the beginning of a word or the consonant sound at the end of the word.) Once the rules are clear, divide the class in two teams and ask one student from each team to come to the front of the class. When you say a word, the students must point to the correct vowel sound (or consonant sound at the beginning or end of a word). The student who points first wins 1 point for their team. The first pair of volunteers then sits down and another pair comes up to listen and point.

5 True or false?

Write a word students have recently met up on the board. Explain the rules of the game. You will say a sentence about the word and students must stand up if it's true or stay sitting if it's false. Possible sentences to use are:

1 'The vowel sound in (say a word) is this.' (Point to a vowel or diphthong symbol on the chart.)

2 'The consonant sound at the start of (say a word) is this.' (Point to a consonant symbol on the chart.)

3 'The consonant sound at the end of (say a word) is this.' (Point to a consonant symbol on the chart.)

4 'There is a schwa sound in the word (say a word). ' (Point to the /ə/ symbol on the chart.)

Instead of getting students to stand up and sit down, you can ask them all to stand up at the start of the game and jump to the right for true and to the left for false. Those who make a mistake must sit down. The last student left standing is the winner.

6 Tap it out

Tap out whole words on the chart with a finger or pen symbol by symbol, and get the class to sound out the symbols as you tap them, and then say the whole word at the end. Once students have got the idea, divide the class into two teams. Tap out a word on the chart and ask one runner from each team to run up to the front of the class, write the word up on the board, and then say it. The first student to do so wins 1 point for their team. The first pair of runners then sits down and another pair watches you tap out a new word and then runs up to the board to write it and say it. (Once students have got the idea of this game, they can do a 'tap it out' dictation. Each student must 'send' ten secret words for their classmate to write down simply by tapping out the symbols on their phonetic chart, without saying anything. At the end of the dictation students should compare the words their partner sent and the words they received.)

7 Sound ping-pong

Divide the class into two teams. Point to a symbol on the chart. Ask a student from Team A to say a word with that sound in it. If he/she does so correctly,

ask a student from Team B to say a different word with that same sound in it. Go on with the same sound, alternating from one team to the other, until a team makes a mistake or can't think of a new word with that sound. The other team gets 1 point at that stage. Then start a new ping-pong 'volley' with a different sound symbol.

8 Hear and show

On the board write a number of minimal pairs focusing on the same two problem sounds (e.g. ship/sheep, slip/sleep, bin/bean, etc.) Point to the symbols on the chart (e.g. /ɪ/ and /iː/) say them, and point to the words on the board and say them to clarify the difference between the words in each pair. Ask students to copy these words down on slips of paper – one word on each slip. When students are ready, say one of the words on the board list, this time without pointing either to the word or to the corresponding symbol on the chart. Students must listen and quickly hold up their slip with the correct word on it. Any students who hold up the wrong slip are out of the game. Point to the word on the board and say it again, and point to the symbol on the chart and say it once more, to clarify if necessary. (Students who are 'out of the game' can help you look out for students who make mistakes later on, with other words on the list.) The student who is left once all other students are 'out of the game' is the winner.

9 Sound brainstorm

Point to a symbol on the chart and ask students in groups to brainstorm as many words they can think of with that sound in them. The group with the longest correct list is the winner.

10 Sound spelling brainstorm

Point to a symbol on the chart and ask students in groups to brainstorm as many different ways of spelling that sound that they can think of and to make a list with one example word for each spelling pattern. The group with the longest correct list is the winner.

11 Sound sorting dictation

Ask students to copy two or three symbols that you point to on the chart in a two or three column table in their exercise books. Then get students to listen to a list of words containing

these sounds as you dictate them, and to write the words in the correct sound column(s) in their table. Alternatively use words on cards that you flash up in front of the class, and which students must copy in the correct sound column(s) in their table. (You can read the words aloud, or not, as you flash the wordcards – depending on whether you want the activity focus to be on reading + listening or on reading + audio memory.)

Phonetic learner training

1 Encourage students to use phonetic symbols for noting down the pronunciation of new words which are problematic to say. When you make a vocabulary list on the board, write up the phonetics in a different colour next to problematic words for students to copy down into their exercise books.

2 Encourage students to read the phonetic symbols in dictionary entries to find out how to say new words. (Note that each dictionary will have small variations in how it notes different sounds. The pronunciation will be different of course in a dictionary for students of British English and a dictionary for students of American English.)

I hope this all sounds useful and interesting and helps you to bring my phonetic colour chart to life with the students in your classroom!

Bill Bowler

SCHOLASTIC

Bill Bowler's Phonetic Colour Chart

For use with Mary Glasgow Timesaver Pronunciation Activities

æ	eɪ	aɪ	ɔɪ	əʊ	aʊ	eə
e	iː	e	ʌ	ʊ	ð	ɜː
ɪ	ɜː	ɑː	ɔː	uː	dʒ	ʒ
				θ	ʃ	tʃ
b	d	g	v	z	l	r
h	p	t	k	f	s	

iə eə
ɪ eɪ aʊ
eɪ

ŋ
j

w m n

Colour Key

Voiced Consonants	
Voiceless Consonants	
Double Vowels	
Short Vowels	
Long Vowels	

Letter boxes

1  **Listen and say the alphabet rap.**

> How do you say the ABC?
> a   b   c   d   and   e
> f   g   h   i   j   - you see!
> k   l   m   n   o   and   p
> q   r   s   t   u   and   v
> w   x   y   z   or zee!

> That's how you
> say the A B C!

NOTE: In British English the last letter of the alphabet is pronounced *zed*.
In American English the last letter of the alphabet is pronounced *zee*.

2 **Listen to the names of the people.**

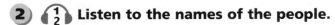

3 **Write the letters of the alphabet in the correct letter boxes to match the sound of the names. (One letter can go in two boxes!)**

4 **Listen and check your answers to exercise 3.**

5 **Fill the gaps in these sentences with the words from the box. Use the sound-alike letter clues to help you.**

> queue   ~~see~~   you   tea
> eye   are   why   be   oh

> She can't
> ~~see~~ (C) me!

1 Who are .... (U)?
2 We'd like two cups of .... (T), please.
3 My .... (I) is all red. It hurts a lot.
4 'Are they English?'
  'Yes, they .... (R).'
5 .... (Y) is she here?
6 There's a long .... (Q) in front of the cinema. Look at all those people!
7 'I cut my hand.'
  '........................... (O) dear!'
8 Hurry up! I don't want to .... (B) late.

Web page sorting

1 🎧 **Listen and repeat the names. Pay attention to the stress (the heavy part) in each name.**

2 **Choose the correct answers.**

1   Where is the stress in the name Freddy?   (Oo)   oO

2   Where is the stress in the name Foster?   Oo   oO

3   Where is the stress in the name Louise?   Oo   oO

4   Where is the stress in the name Lestrange?   Oo   oO

3 🎧 **Listen to these words. Circle the correct stress pattern, Oo or oO.**

1 cartoons   **2 pizzas**   **3 swimming**   **4 dolphin**   **5 thrillers**   **6 lacrosse**
Oo (oO)   Oo   oO   Oo   oO   Oo   oO   Oo   oO   Oo   oO

7 Brazil   **8 kebabs**   **9 Milan**   **10 Poland**   **11 Paris**   **12 giraffe**
Oo   oO   Oo   oO   Oo   oO   Oo   oO   Oo   oO   Oo   oO

4 **Complete Freddy and Louise's web pages 1-6 with the words from exercise 3, according to the stress patterns. Freddy's favourites all have the stress pattern Oo and Louise's favourites all have the stress pattern oO.**

Freddy Foster's Favourites web page

1 Fast Food: *pizzas*

2 Country: ....

3 City: ....

4 Sport: ....

5 Films: ....

6 Animal: ....

Other things Freddy likes:

....
....

LOUISE LESTRANGE'S FAVOURITES WEB PAGE

1 Fast Food: ....

2 Country: ....

3 City: ....

4 Sport: ....

5 Films: ....

6 Animal: ....

Other things Louise likes:
guitars

5 🎧 **1·6** **Listen and choose the correct stress, Oo or oO. Then add the words to the end of Freddy and Louise's web pages in exercise 4.**

1 guitars
Oo   oO

2 Walkmans
Oo   oO

3 cola
Oo   oO

4 machines
Oo   oO

5 football
Oo   oO

6 hotels
Oo   oO

7 shampoo
Oo   oO

8 skateboards
Oo   oO

9 Berlin
Oo   oO

10 Athens
Oo   oO

11 balloons
Oo   oO

12 sardines
Oo   oO

6 **Practise saying the words in exercise 5 with the correct stress.**

7 **Find some more two-syllable words. Mark your words Oo or oO. Use a dictionary or ask your teacher to help you.**
O o - mother, O o - table, O o - English, o O - cassette

Zoo time

1 🎧 $\frac{1}{7}$ **Listen and repeat the names of the zoos. Pay attention to the stress (the heavy part) in each name.**

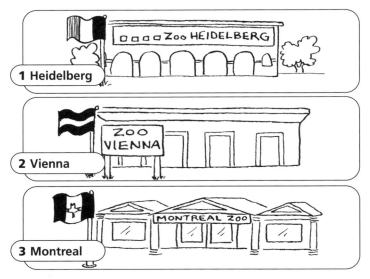

1 Heidelberg

2 Vienna

2 **Choose the correct answers.**

1 Where is the stress in the name Heidelberg?

(Ooo)   oOo   ooO

2 Where is the stress in the name Vienna?

Ooo   oOo   ooO

3 Where is the stress in the name Montreal?

Ooo   oOo   ooO

3 Montreal

3 🎧 $\frac{1}{8}$ **Listen to these animal names. Circle the correct stress pattern, Ooo, oOo or ooO.**

1 koala   Ooo (oOo) ooO

2 kangaroo   Ooo oOo ooO

3 buffalo   Ooo oOo ooO

4 octopus   Ooo oOo ooO

5 flamingo   Ooo oOo ooO

6 polar bear   Ooo oOo ooO

7 antelope   Ooo oOo ooO

8 elephant   Ooo oOo ooO

9 chimpanzee   Ooo oOo ooO

10 gorilla   Ooo oOo ooO

11 piranha   Ooo oOo ooO

12 crocodile   Ooo oOo ooO

4 Put the animals into the correct zoo according to the stress patterns. Which zoo has the most animals? Which has the least?

1 Heidelberg	2 Vienna	3 Montreal
	koala	

5 Listen and mark the words Ooo, oOo or ooO.

○oo
1 cinema

2 hamburger

3 magazine

4 DVD

5 chewing gum

6 basketball

7 spaghetti

8 lemonade

9 bananas

10 margarine

11 lollipop

12 rollerblades

6 Practise saying the words in exercise 5 with the correct stress.

7 Find some more three-syllable words. Mark your words Ooo, oOo or ooO. Use a dictionary or ask your teacher to help you.
O o o - telephone, o O o - computer, o o O - submarine

Sound like Tarzan

1 🎧 **¹⁄₁₀** **Schwa /ə/ is the most common vowel sound in English. Listen to Tarzan saying it.**

/ə/ /ə/ /ə/

2 **Read the instructions and practise making the schwa sound /ə/ like Tarzan.**

> 1 Relax your face and open your mouth a little.
> 2 Imagine someone pushes you gently in the stomach.
> 3 Make the sound as small and as short as you can! (The sound /ɜː/ is a long schwa.)

3 🎧 **¹⁄₁₁** **Listen and mark the stress in these words like this ◡. Listen again and underline the schwa sounds in the words.**

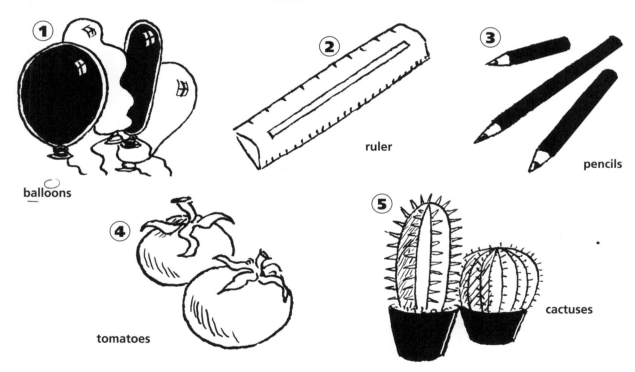

1 balloons

2 ruler

3 pencils

4 tomatoes

5 cactuses

4 **Practise saying the words in exercise 3 aloud. Pay attention to the stresses and the schwas.**

5 **Chose the correct answers to complete the rules.**

> 1 Schwa comes in **stressed / unstressed** parts of words.
> 2 Schwa is a **strong / weak** sound.
> 3 There **is / isn't** a special spelling for the sound schwa.
> 4 Schwa **can / cannot** replace all the written vowels - a, e, i, o, and u.
> 5 Schwa **is / isn't** a typical sound in English.

6 Listen to these words twice. First mark the stresses like this ◯. Then underline the schwa sounds.

1 fossil

2 potatoes

3 teacher

4 cassette

5 sugar

6 photograph

7 doctor

8 acrobats

9 circus

10 banana

7 Practise saying the words in exercise 6 aloud. Pay attention to the stresses and the schwas.

Different habits

1  **Listen and repeat the names. Pay attention to the** /s/, /z/ **and** /ɪz/ **sounds.**

| 1 Chris /s/ | 2 James /z/ | 3 Mercedes /ɪz/ |

2  **Listen to the headless sentences. Pay attention to the sound of the -s and -es verb endings. Is it** /s/, /z/ **or** /ɪz/**?**

1	..........*James*..........	**reads** a lot of magazines.
2	....	**catches** the bus to school every morning.
3	....	**dances** a lot.
4	....	**draws** a lot.
5	....	**eats** a lot of fruit.
6	....	**goes** out on Friday nights.
7	....	**laughs** a lot.
8	....	**loves** art lessons.
9	....	**phones** a friend every day.
10	....	**plays** a lot of tennis.
11	....	**revises** a lot before exams.
12	....	**sleeps** eight hours every night.
13	....	**swims** a lot.
14	....	**wakes** up at seven o'clock every morning.
15	....	**washes** the dog every weekend.

3 Complete the headless sentences in exercise 2 with Chris, James or Mercedes to match the sound of the verb endings.
1 James reads a lot of magazines.

4  are some more Present Simple verbs. How do you pronounce the ending? Is it /s/, /z/ or /ɪz/? Listen and tick the correct box each time.

		/s/	/z/	/ɪz/
1	drinks	✔	☐	☐
2	kisses	☐	☐	☐
3	lives	☐	☐	☐
4	sends	☐	☐	☐
5	watches	☐	☐	☐
6	writes	☐	☐	☐

5 Write more sentences about Chris, James and Mercedes with the verbs from exercise 4. The pronunciation of the verb endings must match the names.

Chris drinks cola every day. ....

....

....

....

....

....

6 Read your sentences aloud to your classmates. Pay attention to the pronunciation of the -*s* and -*es* verb endings.

The picnic

1 🎧 $\frac{1}{16}$ **Listen and repeat the three family names. Pay attention to the /s/, /z/ and /ɪz/ sounds.**

1 The Potts family /s/   **2 The Deeds family** /z/   **3 The Aziz family** /ɪz/

2 🎧 $\frac{1}{17}$ **Listen and repeat the words. Pay attention to the sound of the plural endings. Are they /s/, /z/ or /ɪz/?**

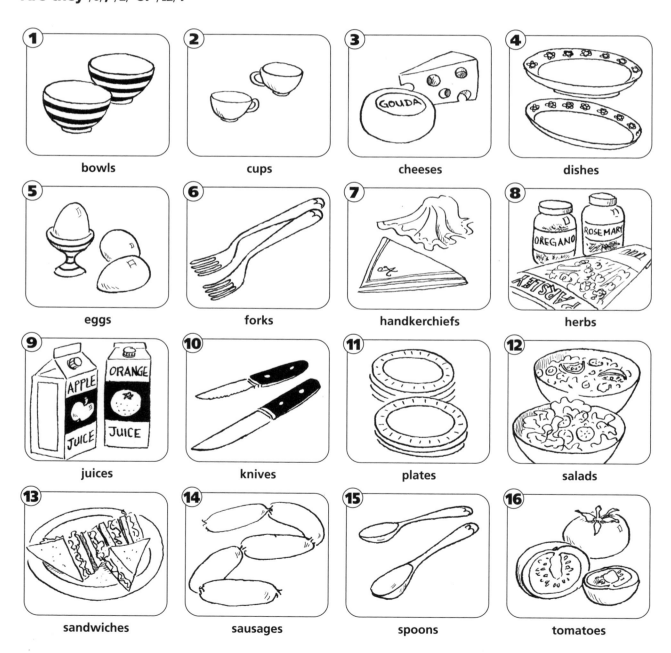

1 bowls	**2** cups	**3** cheeses	**4** dishes
5 eggs	**6** forks	**7** handkerchiefs	**8** herbs
9 juices	**10** knives	**11** plates	**12** salads
13 sandwiches	**14** sausages	**15** spoons	**16** tomatoes

3 What does each family take to the picnic? Write the words from exercise 2 in the correct picnic basket. The sound of the -*s* and -*es* plural endings must match the family names.

1 Potts /s/

POTTS

bowls

DEEDS

2 Deeds /z/

AZIZ

3 Aziz /ɪz/

4 Which family is taking the most things to the picnic? Which family is taking the fewest?

5 Here are some more plural words. Do they end in /s/, /z/ or /ɪz/? Listen and tick the correct box each time.

		/s/	/z/	/ɪz/			/s/	/z/	/ɪz/
1	boxes	☐	☐	☐	8	oranges	☐	☐	☐
2	brushes	☐	☐	☐	9	pubs	☐	☐	☐
3	buses	☐	☐	☐	10	sandals	☐	☐	☐
4	cats	☐	☐	☐	11	scarves	☐	☐	☐
5	cards	☐	☐	☐	12	shirts	☐	☐	☐
6	dogs	☐	☐	☐	13	shoes	☐	☐	☐
7	gloves	☐	☐	☐	14	watches	☐	☐	☐

6 Write some sentences using the words in exercise 5.
Mr Potts likes cats.
Mrs Deeds plays cards.
Delia Deeds loves dogs.
Ali Aziz has got a lot of watches.

7 Read your sentences aloud to your classmates. Pay attention to the pronunciation of the -*s* and -*es* plural endings.

What did they do?

1 🎧 (1/19) **Listen and repeat the names. Pay attention to the** /t/**,** /d/ **and** /ɪd/ **sounds.**

1 Pat /t/

2 Bud /d/

3 Astrid /ɪd/

2 🎧 (1/20) **Listen to the headless sentences. Pay attention to the sound of the** -*d* **and** -*ed* **verb endings. Are they** /t/**,** /d/ **or** /ɪd/ **?**

No meat for me.

1 ....*Pat*........ **cooked** a nice breakfast this morning.

2 .... **decided** to become a vegetarian last year.

3 .... **enjoyed** going to a rock concert on Saturday.

4 .... **kissed** someone at a party last night.

5 .... **laughed** at some funny stories last week.

6 .... **lived** in France for a year.

7 .... **painted** a great picture last month.

8 .... **phoned** a friend at lunchtime.

9 .... **waited** an hour in front of the cinema for tickets.

10 .... **watched** a good programme on TV yesterday.

11 .... **climbed** up a mountain on Saturday.

12 .... **started** aerobics classes last month.

13 .... **travelled** around Spain last summer.

14 .... **wanted** a new computer for Christmas.

15 .... **washed** all the dishes after lunch last Sunday.

3 Complete the headless sentences in exercise 2 with the names from exercise 1 to match the sound of the -*d* and -*ed* verb endings.

1 Pat cooked a nice breakfast this morning.

4 Here are some more Past Simple -*ed* verbs. Do they end in /t/, /d/ or /ɪd/? Listen and tick the correct box each time.

		/t/	/d/	/ɪd/
1	asked	✔		
2	arranged			
3	invited			
4	mended			
5	organised			
6	stopped			

5 Write some more sentences about Pat, Bud and Astrid with the verbs from exercise 4. The -*d* and -*ed* verb endings must match the names.

Pat asked the teacher a question.

....

....

....

....

6 Read your sentences aloud to your classmates. Pay attention to the pronunciation of the -*d* and -*ed* verb endings.

How did they feel?

1 🎧 **1/22 Listen and repeat the names. Pay attention to the /t/, /d/ and /ɪd/ sounds.**

1 Pete /t/

2 Rod /d/

3 David /ɪd/

2 🎧 **1/23 Listen to the pronunciation of the -ed adjective endings. Are they /t/, /d/ or /ɪd/?**

		/t/	/d/	/ɪd/			/t/	/d/	/ɪd/
1	surprised	☐	☐	☐	6	disappointed	☐	☐	☐
2	shocked	☐	☐	☐	7	annoyed	☐	☐	☐
3	disgusted	☐	☐	☐	8	frightened	☐	☐	☐
4	embarrassed	☐	☐	☐	9	bored	☐	☐	☐
5	depressed	☐	☐	☐	10	excited	☐	☐	☐

3 **Are these sentences correct or incorrect? The names must match the sound of the -ed adjective endings.**

1 Rod was surprised when I came to see him without phoning.
.....*correct*.....

2 David was shocked when his girlfriend suddenly left him.
.....*incorrect*.....

3 Pete was bored when his mother took him shopping.
....

4 Pete was depressed when he failed an exam. ....

5 David was embarrassed when his mother kissed him.
....

6 Pete was disgusted when he found a worm in the apple he was eating. ....

7 David was disappointed when his team didn't win the football match. ....

8 Rod was annoyed when his brother took his Walkman without asking. ....

9 Pete was frightened when he was in the house alone one night.
....

10 Rod was excited when he went on holiday to America. ....

4 🎧 **Listen to the sentences from exercise 3 and check your answers.**

5 **Rewrite the incorrect sentences with the correct names.**

2 Pete was shocked when his girlfriend suddenly left him.

6 🎧 **Here are some more *-ed* adjectives. Do they end in** /t/, /d/ **or** /ɪd/**? Listen and then complete the boxes.**

1 confused   **2 exhausted**   **3 scared**   **4 interested**

5 stressed   **6 amazed**   **7 relaxed**   **8 worried**

/t/	/d/	/ɪd/
	confused	

7 **Write some more sentences about Pete, Rod and David with the adjectives from exercise 6. The pronunciation of the adjective endings must match the names.**

David was exhausted after staying up all night.

8 **Read your sentences aloud to your classmates. Pay attention to the pronunciation of the adjective endings.**

Time for a rhyme

1 Listen to the pairs of rhyming words. Then practise saying them.

1		2	
eye	fly	hour	shower

3		4	
two	shoe	break	make

5		6	
please	keys	door	four

Juliet, my pet.

Romeo, please don't go!

2 Listen to these words. Match each word with a rhyming pair in exercise 1.

1 new ...3...   2 cry ....   3 cheese ....   4 more ....   5 flower ....   6 ache ....

3 Complete each crazy two-line poem with a group of three rhyming words from exercises 1 and 2. Look at the pictures to help you.

1 There's a ...fly... in my ...eye...,
  I think I'll ...cry...!

2 After my .... in an ....
  I'll smell like a ....

3 Where's my second .... ?
  I know I've got ....

4 Stop singing. Take a ....!
  You .... my head ....

5 Give me some money to buy some .... ,
  And give me the car................ , ...

6 There are .... or ....
  People at the ....

4 Practise saying the crazy two-line poems in exercise 3 aloud.

Sound-alike pairs

1 Listen to the sound-alike pairs.

 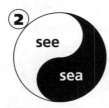 

1 here / hear 2 see / sea 3 sun / son

4 your / you're 5 two / too 6 where's / wears

2 Complete the pairs of sentences with the sound-alike pairs from exercise 1. (Be careful to put each word in the correct sentence!)

1 a I have one ...*son*... and two daughters.
b The ...*sun*... is very hot today!

4 a She can't ....
b The .... is very blue today.

2 a She's got .... cats.
b I like Picasso, ...

5 a Is that .... car?
b .... American!

3 a Speak louder, I can't .... you.
b Come .... !

6 a .... the toilet?
b She .... jeans every day.

3 Circle the correct sound-alike word in each sentence.

1 I'll see you in an **our** / **hour**
2 There's something in my **eye** / **I** .
3 I **read** / **red** a good book yesterday.
4 Can you **write** / **right** your name here?

5 How can a cat wash **it's** / **its** ears?
6 I **know** / **no** you!
7 Who's **there** / **their** father?
8 I've got a **knew** / **new** mobile phone.

4 Listen and say the sound-alike words in exercise 3.

5 Complete the sentences with the sound-alike words you didn't use in exercise 3.

1 That's ...*our*... house.
2 She's wearing a bright .... dress.
3 .... like dancing.
4 It's on the .... , not the left!

5 .... my birthday today.
6 .... thanks. I don't want a cola.
7 I .... the answers to all the questions in the test yesterday.
8 ....'s someone on the phone for you.

Magic letters e and i

1 🎧 (1/30) **When we put *e* at the end of a word ending in consonant + vowel + consonant we don't pronounce the *e*, but it often changes the vowel in a magical way. Listen to these sounds and words.**

/æ/ hat ➜ /eɪ/ hate

/ɪ/ kit ➜ /aɪ/ kite

/e/ pet ➜ /iː/ Pete

/ɒ/ rob ➜ /əʊ/ robe

/ʌ/ cut ➜ /juː/ cute

2 **Listen to the words in exercise 1 again and choose the correct rule.**

1 The magic e makes the short vowels change into the alphabet letter sounds *a, e, i, o* and *u*. ☐

2 The magic e makes the vowels change from long vowels into short vowel sounds. ☐

3 🎧 (1/31) **Look at the words and mark them S (short vowel) or A (alphabet letter sound). Then listen and check your answers.**

1 angry ..S..	3 b**o**ttle	5 h**o**me	7 m**a**ke	9 th**e**se ....
2 b**i**g	4 comp**u**ter	6 l**e**tter	8 s**u**n	10 t**i**me ....

4 🎧 (1/32) **The letter *i* often changes short vowels in the same way. Listen to the words.**

1 hat	/æ/ ➜	hating	/eɪ/	3 bit	/ɪ/ ➜	biting	/aɪ/
2 not	/ɒ/ ➜	notice	/əʊ/	4 cub	/ʌ/ ➜	cubic	/juː/

5 **Read the rules and then write the *-er -est* or *-ing* form of the words.**

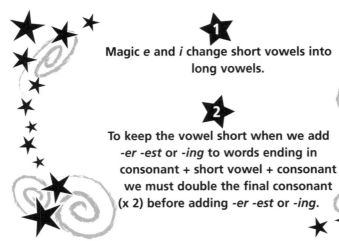

★ **1**
Magic e and i change short vowels into long vowels.

★ **2**
To keep the vowel short when we add *-er -est* or *-ing* to words ending in consonant + short vowel + consonant we must double the final consonant (x 2) before adding *-er -est* or *-ing*.

1 cut + -ing ......*cutting*......
2 swim + -ing ....
3 shop + -ing ....
4 forget + -ing ....
5 clap + -ing ....
6 sad + -er ....
7 hot + -est ....
8 slim + -er ....
9 run + -er ....
10 travel + -er ....

6 🎧 (1/33) **Listen and practise the pairs of words in exercise 5.**

Silent letter clover

1  Look at the clover leaves. Which words below them have got silent letters? Listen and cross out the silent letters. Be careful – some words haven't got silent letters!

 b
thumb
lamb
bomb
comb

 w
answer
write
who
whole

 **k**
knife
knock
know
knit

 h
spaghetti
ghost
hello
honest

A four-leafed clover is lucky. Most clover has only three leaves.

u
guess
guitar
biscuit
building

t
castle
listen
Christmas
whistle

i
fruit
business
friend
suit

l
half
would
should
shoulder

2 How many lucky clover leaves are there with four words with silent letters?

3 Say the words in exercise 1. Take care not to sound the silent letters.

4 Read the silly sentences and cross out the silent letters. Then practise them. How fast can you say them? Take care not to sound the silent letters.

1 She was combing her hair when a bomb killed her pet lamb and she hurt her thumb.

2 He knew she was knitting when he took his knife and knocked on the door.

3 Who can write the whole answer?

4 To be honest, I've never seen a ghost eat spaghetti.

5 I guess I left my guitar and my biscuits in the building.

6 Listen! Someone's whistling a Christmas carol in the castle.

7 I wore a suit to see my friend in the fruit business.

5  Listen to the words (1-5). Then match them with the silent letters below (a-e).

1 cupboard

2 sign

3 autumn

4 island

5 scissors

| **a** silent *n* | **b** silent *c* | **c** silent *g* | **d** silent *p* | **e** silent *s* |

6 Practise saying the words in exercise 5. Take care not to sound the silent letters.

7 Do you know any other words with silent letters? What are they? Make a list.
silent c: muscle

8 Write some silly sentences with your words and practise saying them aloud.

Clothes words

1 **1 36** **Listen to the clothes words and pay attention to the sound of the underlined letters.**

1 /iː/ j<u>ea</u>ns

3 /ɑː/ sc<u>ar</u>f

5 /uː/ sh<u>oe</u>s

2 /ɜː/ sk<u>ir</u>t

4 /ɔː/ sh<u>or</u>ts

2 **1 37** **Listen and say the sounds. Make them long.**

3 **Practise saying the clothes words in exercise 1. Pay attention to the vowel sounds.**

4 **1 38** **Listen to the words in the box. Put the words into the suitcases, according to the sound (not the spelling!) of the underlined letters.**

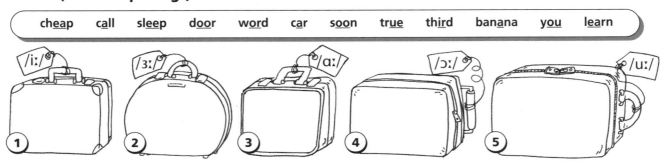

| ch<u>ea</u>p | c<u>a</u>ll | sl<u>ee</u>p | d<u>oo</u>r | w<u>or</u>d | c<u>ar</u> | s<u>oo</u>n | tr<u>ue</u> | th<u>ir</u>d | ban<u>a</u>na | y<u>ou</u> | l<u>ear</u>n |

/iː/ 1   /ɜː/ 2   /ɑː/ 3   /ɔː/ 4   /uː/ 5

5 **Can you think of at least 5 more words with these sounds in them? (One word for each sound.) Use a dictionary or ask your teacher to check the sounds. Add them to the suitcases in exercise 4.**

6 **Match a word from the box with each word in phonetic code.**

| bead | bird | <u>bored</u> | far | four | fur | he | hard | heard | tea | two | who |

1	/bɔːd/	4	/biːd/	7	/fɑː/	10	/hɜːd/
	bored						
2	/bɜːd/	5	/fɜː/	8	/hiː/	11	/tuː/
3	/hɑːd/	6	/fɔː/	9	/huː/	12	/tiː/

Food words

1 🎧 **Listen to the food words and pay attention to the sounds of the underlined letters.**

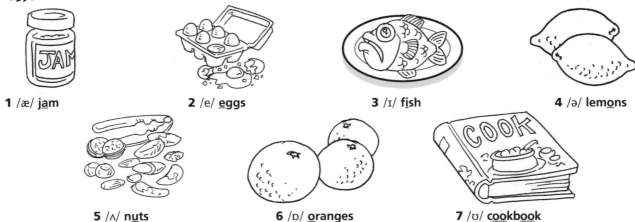

1 /æ/ j<u>a</u>m   2 /e/ <u>e</u>ggs   3 /ɪ/ f<u>i</u>sh   4 /ə/ lem<u>o</u>ns

5 /ʌ/ n<u>u</u>ts   6 /ɒ/ <u>o</u>ranges   7 /ʊ/ c<u>oo</u>kb<u>oo</u>k

2 🎧 **Listen and say the sounds. Make them short.**

3 **Practise saying the food words in exercise 1. Pay attention to the vowel sounds.**

4 🎧 **Listen to the words in the box. Put the words into the shopping bags, according to the sound (not the spelling!) of the underlined letters.**

| <u>a</u>gain | m<u>a</u>ny | b<u>a</u>nk | br<u>ea</u>d | f<u>oo</u>t | w<u>a</u>nt | c<u>u</u>p | t<u>i</u>cket | y<u>ou</u>ng | w<u>o</u>nderful | d<u>i</u>nner | c<u>ou</u>ld |

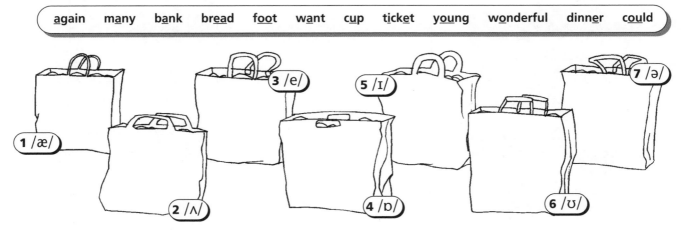

3 /e/   5 /ɪ/   7 /ə/

1 /æ/

2 /ʌ/   4 /ɒ/   6 /ʊ/

5 **Can you think of at least 7 more words with these sounds in them? (One word for each sound.) Use a dictionary or ask your teacher to check the sounds. Add them to the shopping bags in exercise 4.**

6 **Match a word from the box with each word in phonetic code.**

| bell | better | ~~bull~~ | butter | fat | foot | had | head | hit | hot | not | nut |

1 /bʊl/
    bull
....

2 /bel/
....

3 /'betə/
....

4 /'bʌtə/
....

5 /fʊt/
....

6 /fæt/
....

7 /hed/
....

8 /hæd/
....

9 /hɒt/
....

10 /hɪt/
....

11 /nɒt/
....

12 /nʌt/
....

Sheep or ship?

1 🎧 1/42 **Listen to the pairs of words. Pay attention to the sound of the underlined letters.**

1 /iː/ sh<u>ee</u>p

2 /ɪ/ sh<u>i</u>p

3 /uː/ p<u>oo</u>l

4 /ʊ/ p<u>u</u>ll

5 /ɑː/ h<u>ea</u>rt

6 /ʌ/ h<u>u</u>t

7 /ɔː/ sp<u>or</u>ts

8 /ɒ/ sp<u>o</u>ts

9 /ɜː/ h<u>er</u>s

10 /ə/ h<u>a</u>s

2 🎧 1/43 **Listen and say the sounds.**

3 **Practise saying the pairs of words in exercise 1. Pay attention to the vowel sounds.**

4 🎧 1/44 **Listen to the sentences and circle the correct word each time.**

1   Where's that **sheep / ship**?

2   Does that sign say '**pool**' / '**pull**'?

3   That **heart / hut** is big and red.

4   I don't like **sports / spots**.

5   Did you say '**hers**' / '**has**'?

6   Can I have some white **beans / bins**?

7   **Luke / Look**, is that your sister?

8   I've got two **barns / buns**.

9   I like Spanish **ports / pots**.

10   Is that word '**urn**' / '**an**'?

5 You will hear three words each time. Circle the word you hear twice.

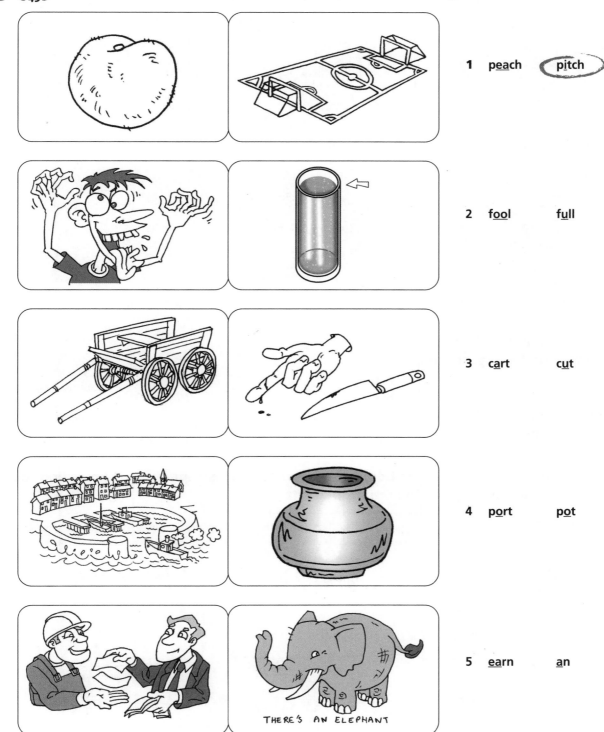

1 peach   pitch

2 fool   full

3 cart   cut

4 port   pot

5 earn   an

THERE'S AN ELEPHANT

6 Practise saying the words in exercise 5. Pay attention to the vowel sounds.

7 Work in pairs. Take turns to say different words from exercises 1 and 5. Your partner must listen and say *long* or *short* each time. Tell your partner when he/she is correct.

Sports sounds

1 🎧 $\frac{1}{46}$ **Listen to the sports words and pay attention to the sound of the underlined letters.**

1 /h/ <u>h</u>orse-riding

2 /p/ <u>p</u>ress-ups

3 /t/ <u>t</u>ennis

4 /k/ <u>c</u>limbing

5 /f/ <u>f</u>ootball

6 /s/ <u>s</u>wimming

2 🎧 $\frac{1}{47}$ **Listen and make the sounds. Don't use your voice.**

3 **Practise saying the sports words in exercise 1. Pay attention to the underlined sounds.**

Put your hand on your voice box when you say these sounds. Your voice box mustn't vibrate for voiceless sounds.

4 🎧 $\frac{1}{48}$ **Listen to the words in the box. Put the words into the sports bags according to the sound (not the spelling!) of the underlined letters.**

<u>ph</u>one   <u>k</u>ey   <u>c</u>inema   ba<u>ck</u>   <u>h</u>ello   Mi<u>ss</u>   co<u>ff</u>ee   <u>t</u>ime   <u>sh</u>opping   be<u>tt</u>er   be<u>h</u>ind   <u>ch</u>emist

1 /k/

2 /h/

3 /p/

4 /f/

5 /s/

6 /t/

5 **Can you think of at least 6 more words with these different sounds in them? (One word for each sound.) Use a dictionary or ask your teacher to check the sounds. Add them to the sports bags in exercise 4.**

Job sounds

1 🔊 $\frac{1}{49}$ **Listen to the job words and pay attention to the sound of the underlined letters.**

1 /b/ **b**odyguard   **2** /d/ **d**octor   **3** /g/ **g**ardener   **4** /v/ **v**et   **5** /z/ **z**ookeeper

6 /l/ **l**ifeguard   **7** /r/ **r**apper   **8** /w/ **w**aiter   **9** /m/ **m**echanic   **10** /n/ **n**urse

2 🔊 $\frac{1}{50}$ **Listen and say the sounds. Use your voice.**

3 **Practise saying the job words in exercise 1. Pay attention to the underlined letters.**

> Put your hand on your voice box when you say these sounds. It vibrates when you use your voice.

4 🔊 $\frac{1}{51}$ **Listen to the words in the box. Put the words into the money boxes, according to the sound (not the spelling!) of the underlined letters.**

| clever | football | egg | saddest | carry | rubber | busy |
| make | one | club | bad | swimmer | colour | runner | water |

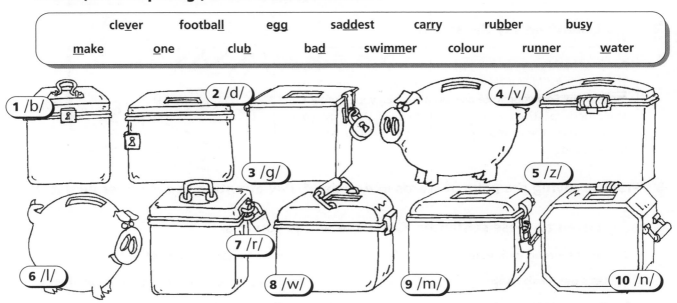

1 /b/   2 /d/   3 /g/   4 /v/   5 /z/   6 /l/   7 /r/   8 /w/   9 /m/   10 /n/

5 **Can you think of at least 10 more words with these different sounds in them? (One word for each sound.) Use a dictionary or ask your teacher to check the sounds. Add them to the money boxes in exercise 4.**

Cab or cap?

1 🎧 1/52 **Listen to the pairs of words. Pay attention to the sounds of the underlined letters.**

 **1** /b/ ca**b**

2 /p/ ca**p**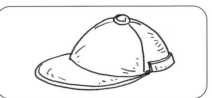

 **3** /d/ be**d**

4 /t/ be**t**

 **5** /g/ ba**g**

6 /k/ bac**k**

 **7** /v/ li**v**e

8 /f/ li**f**e

 **9** /z/ **z**oo

10 /s/ **S**ue

2 🎧 1/53 **Listen and say the sounds.**

Put your hand on your voice box when you say these sounds. The sounds /b/ /d/ /g/ /v/ and /z/ are voiced. Use your voice to make them. Feel your voice box vibrate when you say them. The sounds /p/ /t/ /k/ /f/ and /s/ are voiceless. Don't use your voice to make them. Your voice box doesn't vibrate to make these sounds.

3 **Practise saying the pairs of words in exercise 1. Pay attention to the underlined letters.**

4 🎧 1/54 **Listen to these sentences. Circle the words you hear.**

1 What's wrong with your **bag / back**?

2 Let's get a **cab / cap**!

3 Do you want a **bed / bet**?

4 That's **live / life**!

5 Her T-shirt has '**Zoo**' / '**Sue**' on it.

6 Have you seen my **goat / coat**?

7 There are lots of wild **bears / pears** here.

8 This **drain / train** is very smelly.

9 Do you like my new **van / fan**?

10 What's the **prize / price**?

5 **1 55** **You will hear three words each time. Circle the word you hear twice.**

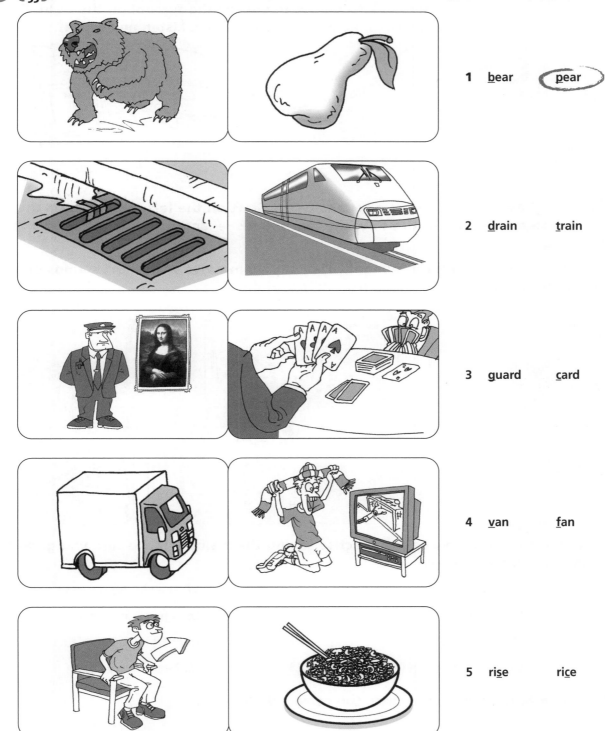

1 <u>b</u>ear   (<u>p</u>ear)

2 <u>d</u>rain   <u>t</u>rain

3 <u>g</u>uard   <u>c</u>ard

4 <u>v</u>an   <u>f</u>an

5 ri<u>s</u>e   ri<u>c</u>e

6 Practise saying the words in exercise 5. Pay attention to the underlined letters.

7 Work in pairs. Take turns to say different words from exercises 1 and 5. Your partner must listen and say *voiced* or *voiceless* each time. Tell your partner when he/she is correct.

Phonetic hang-gliding

1 🎧 $\frac{1}{56}$ **Look to the left and say the symbol on top of the hill. Then look to the right and say the symbol on the right. Do this twice. Keep the sounds short. Listen and repeat.**

2 🎧 $\frac{1}{57}$ **Now glide between the two sounds twice. Start on the left and finish on the right. Listen and repeat. Notice how the two sounds /e/ and /ɪ/ combine to form the diphthong /eɪ/.**

3 🎧 $\frac{1}{58}$ **Do the same with these symbols. First say them twice with short sounds on the left and right, then do two glides from left to right.**

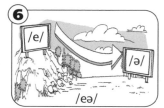

4 🎧 $\frac{1}{59}$ **Listen to the sentences and practise saying them aloud. Make sure you glide on the underlined diphthongs.**

1	/eɪ/	It's a gr<u>ey</u> and r<u>ai</u>ny d<u>ay</u>.	5	/aʊ/	What a nice br<u>ow</u>n c<u>ow</u>!
2	/aɪ/	Is this <u>my</u> apple p<u>ie</u>?	6	/ɪə/	Look h<u>ere</u> - in my <u>ear</u>!
3	/ɔɪ/	That's R<u>oy</u>'s new t<u>oy</u>.	7	/eə/	Her h<u>air</u> is long and f<u>air</u>.
4	/əʊ/	Look at J<u>oe</u>'s big t<u>oe</u>!	8	/ʊə/	Mr M<u>oor</u> is very p<u>oor</u>.

5 🎧 $\frac{1}{60}$ **Listen to the words and circle the correct diphthong.**

1	<u>join</u>	/eɪ/	/aɪ/	/ɔɪ/	5	<u>near</u>	/eə/	/ʊə/	/ɪə/	
2	t<u>own</u>	/əʊ/	/aʊ/	/aɪ/	6	fl<u>own</u>	/əʊ/	/aʊ/	/aɪ/	
3	b<u>ear</u>	/eɪ/	/aɪ/	/eə/	7	ch<u>oir</u>	/eɪ/	/aɪ/	/ɔɪ/	
4	t<u>our</u>	/əʊ/	/ʊə/	/aʊ/	8	<u>our</u>	/əʊ/	/aʊ/	/aɪ/	

6 **Practise saying the words in exercise 5 aloud. Make sure you glide on the underlined diphthongs.**

A fancy dress party

1 🎧 **1 61** **Look at the picture. Then listen to the sounds and words. Pay attention to the sound of the underlined letters.**

3 /ɔɪ/ Superb<u>oy</u>

1 /aɪ/ V<u>i</u>king

2 /eɪ/ sn<u>a</u>ke charmer

4 /əʊ/ R<u>o</u>man

5 /aʊ/ cl<u>ow</u>n

6 /eə/ w<u>ere</u>wolf

7 /ʊə/ t<u>ou</u>rist

8 /ɪə/ Musket<u>ee</u>r

2 **Practise saying the sounds and words in exercise 1. Pay attention to the underlined letters.**

3 🎧 **1 62** **Listen to the words in the box. Put the words into the correct character according to the sound (not the spelling!) of the underlined letters.**

ear	toilet	break	boat	bear	cry	careful	yellow
out	train	here	poor	day	their	eight	

1 /eɪ/ snake charmer   **2** /aɪ/ Viking   **3** /ɔɪ/ Superboy   **4** /əʊ/ Roman

5 /aʊ/ clown   **6** /eə/ werewolf   **7** /ɪə/ Musketeer   **8** /ʊə/ tourist

4 **Match a word from the box with each word in phonetic code.**

beer	boy	buy	near	no	now	pay	poor	pair	toe	tour	toy

1 /nəʊ/
...........no...........

2 /naʊ/
....

3 /nɪə/
....

4 /baɪ/
....

5 /bɪə/
....

6 /bɔɪ/
....

7 /tɔɪ/
....

8 /tʊə/
....

9 /təʊ/
....

10 /peɪ/
....

11 /pʊə/
....

12 /peə/
....

Phonos the alien

1 Phonos comes from the planet Phonetica. They use strange phonetic symbols there. Listen to the sounds and then read the sentences (1-2) and choose the correct answers.

> **1** The sounds /dʒ/ /ʒ/ /ð/ /ŋ/ and /j/ (on the left) are **voiced / voiceless**.
>
> **2** The sounds /tʃ/ /ʃ/ and /θ/ (on the right) are **voiced / voiceless**.

2 Listen to the sounds and the words. Pay attention to the sound of underlined letters.

1 /dʒ/ <u>j</u>am   **2** /tʃ/ <u>ch</u>ess   **3** /ʒ/ televi<u>si</u>on   **4** /ʃ/ <u>sh</u>op

5 /ð/ mo<u>th</u>er   **6** /θ/ <u>th</u>eatre   **7** /ŋ/ si<u>ng</u>   **8** /j/ <u>y</u>oung

3 Practise saying the words in exercise 2. Pay attention to the underlined letters.

4 Match a word from the box with each word in phonetic code.

> chat cheap garage jeep jet sheep shot that thin thing wash watch wing with yacht yet

1 /tʃi:p/ _cheap_	**5** /jet/	**9** /θɪŋ/	**13** /wɪð/
2 /ʃi:p/	**6** /ˈgærɑːʒ/	**10** /θɪn/	**14** /wɪŋ/
3 /dʒi:p/	**7** /jɒt/	**11** /wɒtʃ/	**15** /ðæt/
4 /dʒet/	**8** /ʃɒt/	**12** /wɒʃ/	**16** /tʃæt/

Sam the spy

1 Sam the Spy likes to send messages in phonetic code.
Can you decode the names of countries from his
Phonetic Code Book? Match the words in the box with
the words in phonetic code.

Argentina	Australia	Austria	Brazil
England	France	Germany	Greece
Hungary	Italy	Poland	Turkey

1 /'ɪŋglənd/
.....England.....

2 /'pəʊlənd/
....

3 /'ɒstrɪə/
....

4 /ɒst'reɪlɪə/
....

5 /'dʒɜːmənɪ/
....

6 /frɑːns/
....

7 /griːs/
....

8 /'ɪtəlɪ/
....

9 /'tɜːkɪ /
....

10 /'hʌŋgərɪ/
....

11 /ɑːdʒən'tiːnə/
....

12 /brə'zɪl/
....

2 Now read the Phonetic Code sentences about Sam the Spy and finish decoding them
into English. (Try saying them aloud!)

1 /sæm ðə spaɪ ɪz 'twentɪ yɪəz əʊld/
Sam ...the spy is... twenty ....

2 /hiː kʌmz frəm ɒst'reɪlɪə/
He .... from ....

3 /hiː lɪvz ɪn ə haʊs ɪn 'sɪdnɪ/
.... a .... Sydney.

4 /hiːz θɪn ənd hiːz gɒt red heə/
.... and he's ....

5 /hiː ɪn'dʒɔɪz 'wɒtʃɪŋ 'telɪvɪʒən
.... enjoys .... ,
'pleɪɪŋ kɑːdz ənd 'riːdɪŋ bʊks/
playing .... and ....

6 /hiː lʌvz 'drɪŋkɪŋ dʒuːs/
.... loves ....

7 /hiːz 'verɪ pʊə/
.... very ....

8 /hiː laɪks 'iːtɪŋ fɪʃ/
.... eating ....

9 /hiːz gɒt ə 'gɜːlfrend/
.... got ....

10 /hɜː neimʒ 'sɑːndrə ðə spaɪ/
.... name's Sandra ....

3 🎧 Listen to the sentences in exercise 2 and practise saying them aloud. Look at the phonetics as you say each sentence.

4 Look at this page of phonetic code from Sam's notebook. They are all questions. Can you decode them?

1 /wɒts jə neɪm/
   .... What's your name? ....

2 /haʊ əʊld ə ju/
   ....

3 /wɪtʃ 'læŋwɪdʒɪz djə spiːk/
   ....

4 /weə ɪg'zæktlɪ djə lɪv/
   ....

5 /kən jə dɪs'craɪb jəself/
   ....

6 /wɒt djə laɪk 'duːɪŋ in jə friː taɪm/
   ....

7 /wɒts jə 'feɪvrət fuːd/
   ....

8 /wɒts jə 'feɪvrət drɪŋk/
   ....

9 /haʌ mʌtʃ 'mʌnɪ həv jə gɒt ɒn jə/
   ....

10 /həv jə gɒt ə 'gɜːlfrend ɔːr ə 'bɔɪfrend/
   ....

5 Now answer the questions in exercise 4. Then translate your answers into phonetic code if you can!
   1 My name's …   */maɪ neɪmz …/*

Who killed Sir Benjamin Blue?

1 Last night someone killed Sir Benjamin Blue in his country house.
But who? There were six people in the house at the time.

1 Dr White

2 Lady Mauve

3 Lord Fawn

4 Mrs Turquoise

5 Ms Pink

6 Professor Black

Sir Benjamin Blue

2 (1/66) Inspector Brown is investigating the case. Here are his notes of where people were and what they had with them at the time of the murder. Listen.

poison? sword? pistol? spanner? rope? paper knife?

Suspect	Place	Murder Weapon
Dr White	garage	pistol
Lady Mauve	kitchen	spanner
Lord Fawn	nursery	rope
Mrs Turquoise	hall	paper knife
Ms Pink	library	poison
Professor Black	rose garden	sword

garage

kitchen

nursery

hall

library

rose garden

3 Unfortunately Inspector Brown's notes are all mixed up. Can you sort them out?

Suspect	Place		Murder Weapon	
Dr White	1 ..... *library* ..... /ˈlaɪbrərɪ/		2 .... /ˈpeɪpə naɪf/	
Lady Mauve	3 .... /rəʊz ˈgɑːdən/		4 .... /rəʊp/	
Lord Fawn	5 .... /hɔːl/		6 .... /sɔːd/	
Mrs Turquoise	7 .... /ˈnɜːsərɪ/		8 .... /ˈpɔɪzən/	
Ms Pink	9 .... /ˈkɪtʃən/		10 .... /ˈpɪstəl/	
Professor Black	11 .... /ˈgærɑːʒ/		12 .... /ˈspænə/	

4 Now read what Sir Benjamin Blue wrote in his diary just before he died. It's in phonetic code. Can you decode it?

1 ....
....
....

2 ....
....
....

1 /aɪm ɪn ðə ruːm aɪ lʌvd wen aɪ wəz ə tʃaɪld/

2 /aɪm ˈgəʊɪŋ tə drɪŋk ə naɪs kʌp əv tiː/

5 Can you solve the crime? Complete Inspector Brown's notes. Look at exercises 3 and 4 to help you.

1 *Where was Sir Benjamin when he died?*   Sir Benjamin was in the ....

2 *Who was the murderer?*   The murderer was ....

3 *What did the murderer use?*   The murder weapon was ....

Furniture and furnishing crossword

1 🎧 **1/67** **Match the words in the box with the phonetic code. Listen and check.**

1 /ˈteɪbəl/

.... *table* ....

2 /ˈfaɪəpleɪs/

....

3 /frɪdʒ/

....

4 /tʃeəz/

....

5 /desk/

....

6 /ˈkʌbəd/

....

7 /ˈkʊkə/

....

8 /ˈsəʊfə/

....

9 /læmp/

....

10 /ˈkɑːpɪt/

....

11 /bentʃ/

....

12 /ˈbʊkʃelvz/

....

13 /ˈwɔːdrəʊb/

....

14 /stuːl/

....

15 /ˈdresɪŋ ˌteɪbəl/

....

bench
bookshelves
carpet
cooker
cupboard
chairs
desk
dressing table
fireplace
fridge
lamp
sofa
stool
~~table~~
wardrobe

2 **Look at the picture clues and complete the crossword with the phonetic symbols for the words. Put only one vowel, consonant or diphthong symbol in each square. Don't include stress marks for main stress (') or secondary stress (ˌ).**

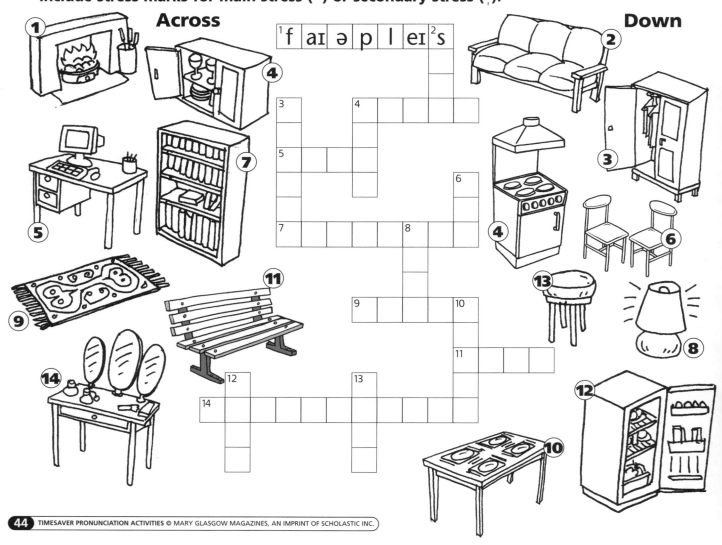

Across / Down

¹f aɪ ə p l eɪ ²s

Andy the Pronunciation Android

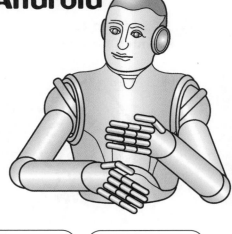

1 Andy the Pronunciation Android is very good at pronouncing English. Match the instructions (1-13) with the pictures of Andy (a-m).

1 Open your mouth a little. ....*a*......

2 Don't use your voice. Whisper! ....

3 Make your lips round. ....

4 Bite your lower lip with your top teeth. ....

5 Open your mouth wide. ....

6 Push air through your mouth. ....

7 Push air through your nose. ....

8 Put your tongue between your teeth. ....

9 Relax your face. ....

10 Spread your lips. Smile! ....

11 Touch your voice box. ....

12 Use your voice! Make sounds and feel your voice box vibrate! ....

13 Close your lips tight. ....

a

b

c

d

e

f

g

h

i

j

k

l

m

2 Listen and check your answers.

3 Work in pairs. Student A does one of Andy's actions and Student B points to the correct picture. Then change roles.

4 Listen and do the actions **only** when the instruction starts with the phrase *Andy the Android says ...* .

5 Work in pairs. Take it in turns to give instructions and do actions. Only do the action if your partner starts the instruction with *Andy the Android says ...* .

Shapes dictation

1 🎧 2/3 **Listen to the pairs of words. The vowel sound /iː/ is long but the vowel sound /ɪ/ is short. Can you hear the difference?**

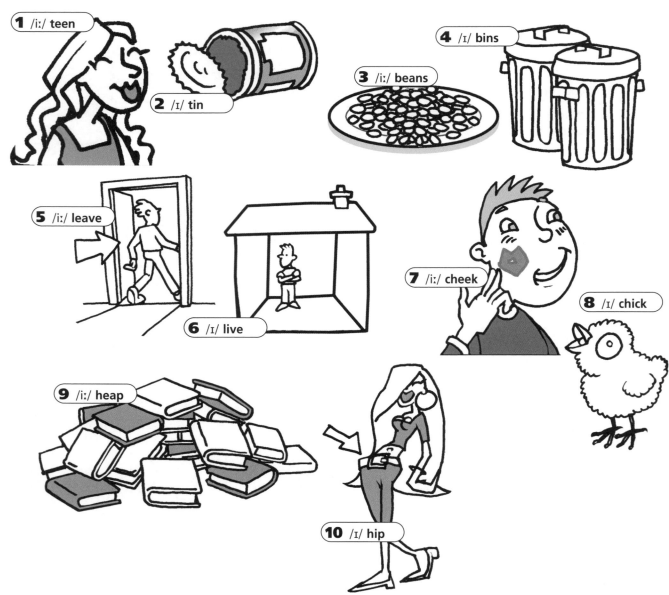

1 /iː/ teen
2 /ɪ/ tin
3 /iː/ beans
4 /ɪ/ bins
5 /iː/ leave
6 /ɪ/ live
7 /iː/ cheek
8 /ɪ/ chick
9 /iː/ heap
10 /ɪ/ hip

2 **Practise saying the pairs of words in exercise 1. Make the vowel sound /iː/ very long. Make the vowel sound /ɪ/ very short.**

3 🎧 2/4 **Listen to these sentences and circle the correct word.**

1 That's not for **teens / tins**.
2 Look at her **cheeks / chicks**.
3 What large **heaps / hips**!
4 Let's **leave / live** here.
5 We've got five **beans / bins**.

6 They are nice **teens / tins**.
7 Don't touch my **heaps / hips**!
8 They're my **cheeks / chicks**.
9 He's got two **heaps / hips**.
10 The **beans / bins** are over there.

4 **Work in pairs. Take turns to say different words from exercise 1. Your partner must listen and say *long* or *short* each time. Tell your partner when he/she is correct.**

5 **Your teacher will give you two Shape Dictation Grid pages. Read the instructions and play the game.**

1 Mark one of the Shape Dictation Grids *Send* and the other *Receive*.

2 On your *Send* page write nine words from exercise 1 in the nine shapes. (You can use some words twice if you want!) Put one word in each shape.

3 Now work in pairs. DON'T show your *Send* page to your partner. Ask and answer about your Shape Dictation Grids. Use the dialogue to help you.

A: *What's in your shape 1?*
B: *'cheek'. What's in your shape 1?*
A: *'live'. What have you got in shape 2?*
B: *'leave'. What have you got in shape 2?*

4 Complete your *Receive* page with your partner's answers. Write the words in the correct shapes.

5 When you finish, compare your *Send* and *Receive* pages. Could you send and receive all the words correctly? If not, practise saying the problem words in exercise 1 again.

Send   Receive

Sound bingo

1 🎧 **²₅ Listen to the pairs of words. The sound /uː/ is long. The sound /ʊ/ is short. Can you hear the difference?**

5 /ʊ/ full

3 /uː/ pool

4 /ʊ/ pull

1 /uː/ suit

2 /ʊ/ soot

6 /uː/ fool

COULD YOU HELP ME?

WHO'D LIKE AN ICE CREAM

12 /ʊ/ hood

11 /uː/ who'd

10 /ʊ/ could

9 /uː/ cooed

7 /uː/ wooed

8 /ʊ/ wood

13 /uː/ shooed

YOU SHOULD STOP SMOKING

14 /ʊ/ should

2 **Complete these pairs of sentences with pairs of words from exercise 1.**

1 a Who wants to swim in the ....*pool*.... ?
   b Don't push the door, ...*pull*.... it!

2 a He .... the dogs away from the injured cat.
   b You .... do more exercise to lose weight.

3 a .... you open the window? It's hot in here.
   b The dove .... at him from the birdcage.

4 a He doesn't know anything, he's a ....
   b I'm .... I can't eat another thing.

5 a Alfonso .... Freda for many years before she agreed to marry him.
   b Their country house was made of ....

6 a After cleaning the fireplace his hands were black with ....
   b He wore a new grey .... to the wedding.

7 a The executioner wore a black .... over his head.
   b .... like some pizza? Peter? Sue? Anyone?

3 **Practise saying the pairs of words in exercise 1. Make the vowel sound /uː/ very long. Make the vowel sound /ʊ/ very short.**

4 🎧 **²₆ Listen to the pairs of words. Circle the word you hear twice each time.**

1 suit / soot   **3** fool / full   **5** cooed / could   **7** who'd / hood

2 pool / pull   **4** wooed / wood   **6** shooed / should

5 **Work in pairs. Take turns to say different words from exercise 1. Your partner must listen and say *long* or *short* each time. Tell your partner when he/she is correct.**

6 Read the instructions and play the games.

Class Sound Bingo

1   On your Class Bingo card write nine words from exercise 1 in the spaces to match the sound symbols. Put one word in each space.

2   Listen to the CD and tick the words you hear. When you have ticked all the words on your card, shout 'Bingo!' The first student in the class who shouts 'Bingo!' (and who has ticked the correct words) is the winner.

Group Sound Bingo

1   Prepare to play Sound Bingo in groups of four, Students A, B, C and D.
    Student A: write all the words from exercise 1 in a numbered list from 1-14. DON'T show the list to the other students in your group.
    Students B, C and D: Individually complete your Group Bingo card with nine different words from exercise 1. Write the words in the spaces to match the sound symbols. Put one word in each space.

2   Play the game.
    Student A: call out the words on your list, slowly and clearly, one by one.
    Students B, C and D: Listen and tick the words you hear. When you have ticked all the words on your card, shout 'Bingo!' The first student in the group who shouts 'Bingo!' (and who has ticked the correct words) is the winner.

3   When you finish, compare student A's list and Student B's, C's and D's Group Sound Bingo cards. Did you say and hear all the words correctly? If not, practise saying the problem words in exercise 1 again.

4   Change roles and play the game again.

Class card

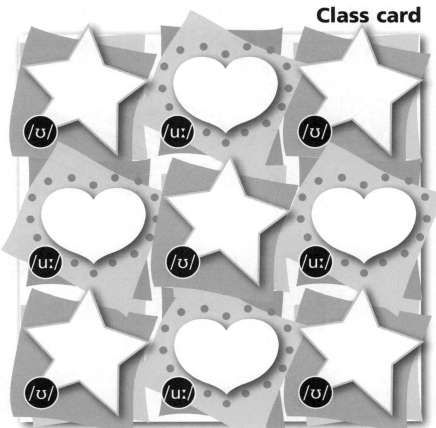

Group card

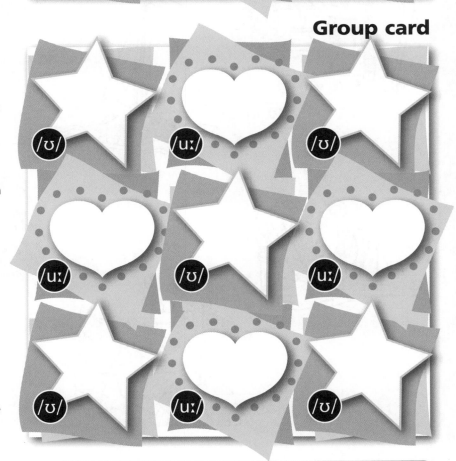

Edit the words

1 🎧 **Listen to the pairs of words. In the words on the left in each pair, the vowel sound is /e/. In the words on the right it is /eɪ/. Can you hear the difference?**

1 /e/ pepper

2 /eɪ/ paper

3 /e/ pen

4 /eɪ/ pain

5 /e/ Len

6 /eɪ/ lane

7 /e/ shed

8 /eɪ/ shade

9 /e/ sell

10 /eɪ/ sail

11 /e/ men

12 /eɪ/ Maine

13 /e/ test

14 /eɪ/ taste

15 /e/ wet

16 /eɪ/ wait

2 **Read the instructions and practise saying the pairs of words in exercise 1.**

1 /e/ is a short sound. Spread your lips wide and open your jaw a little to make this sound. Make the single vowel sounds in the words on the left short.

2 /eɪ/ is a diphthong (double vowel sound). It starts with /e/ and it ends with /ɪ/. Make the double vowel sounds in the words on the right long.

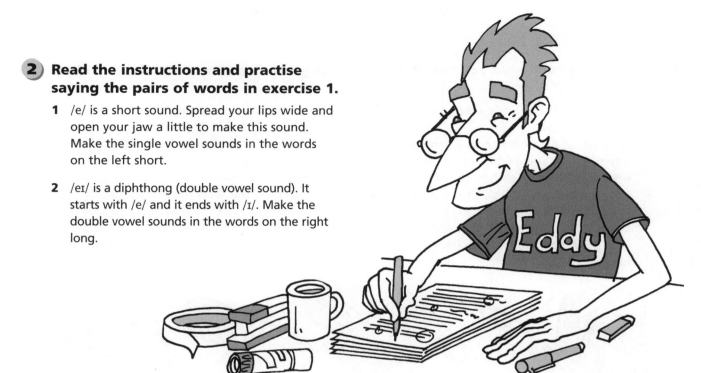

3 (2/8) **Listen to these sentences and circle the word you hear each time.**

1 I bought some **pepper / paper**.

2 He's got a **pen / pain**.

3 That **Len / lane** is really nice.

4 I like sitting in the **shed / shade**.

5 She's **selling / sailing** her boat.

6 She likes **men / Maine**.

7 I'm going to **test / taste** it.

8 The sign has **'Wet' / 'Wait'** on it.

4 **Work in pairs. Take turns to say different words from exercise 1. Your partner must listen and say *single vowel* or *double vowel* each time. Tell your partner when he/she is correct.**

5 (2/9) **Eddy the editor marks the words in the books he edits in different ways. Match the instructions (1-10) with the marks he makes (a-j). Then listen and check your answers.**

1 Box the word dictionary. ....*e*............ **a** dictionary ?

2 Circle the word dictionary. .... **b** "dictionary"

3 Cross out the word dictionary. .... **c** ~~dictionary~~

4 Put a question mark after the word dictionary. .... **d** <u>dictionary</u>

5 Put a tick next to the word dictionary. .... **e** [dictionary]

6 Put an asterisk next to the word dictionary. .... **f** (dictionary)

7 Put an exclamation mark after the word dictionary. .... **g** dictionary*

8 Put the word dictionary in quotation marks. .... **h** dictionary!

9 Rewrite the word dictionary in capital letters. .... **i** DICTIONARY

10 Underline the word dictionary. .... **j** dictionary ✔

6 **Your teacher will give you two Edit the words grids. Read the instructions and play the game.**

1   Mark one of the Edit the words grids *Send* and the other *Receive*.

2   Mark ten of the words on your *Send* grid in different ways using Eddy the Editor's marks from exercise 5. Only use each mark once.

3   Now work in pairs. DON'T show your *Send* page to your partner. Give instructions to your partner to mark ten of the words on his/her *Receive* grid with Eddy the Editor's marks. Use this dialogue to help you.

A: *Box the word* pepper.
B: *OK. Underline the word* Len.
A: *Right. Now rewrite the word* Maine *in capital letters.*

4   Follow your partner's instructions carefully and mark the words on your *Receive* page.

5   When you finish, compare your *Send* and *Receive* pages. Could you send and receive all the instructions correctly? If not, practise saying the problem words in exercise 1 again.

pepper	sell	test	shade
pain	wait	paper	Maine
taste	lane	sail	shed
wet	men	pen	Len

Send
Receive

Picasso's paints

1 🔊 **Listen to these trios of words. In the words on the left the vowel sound is /æ/. In the words in the middle the vowel sound is /ʌ/. In the words on the right the vowel sound is /ɑː/. Can you hear the difference?**

/æ/ cat	/ʌ/ cut	/ɑː/ cart
/æ/ hat	/ʌ/ hut	/ɑː/ heart
/æ/ ban	/ʌ/ bun	/ɑː/ barn
/æ/ cap	/ʌ/ cup	/ɑː/ carp

2 **Read the instructions and practise saying the trios of words in exercise 1.**

1 /æ/ is a short sound. Spread your lips wide and open your jaw to make this sound (like eating an apple). Make the words very short.

2 /ʌ/ is a short sound. Keep your jaw open but relax your lips to make this sound. Make the words very short.

3 /ɑː/ is a long sound. Relax your lips and open your jaw to make this sound. Make the words very long.

3 🔊 **Listen to these sentences and circle the word you hear each time.**

1 She's got a big **hat / heart**.

2 Is this your **bun / barn**?

3 There's a big **cap / carp** over there!

4 I like your **hat / hut**.

5 His **cat's / cart's** very old.

6 These are all my sports **caps / cups**.

4 **Work in pairs. Take turns to say different words from exercise 1. Your partner must listen and point to the word each time. Tell your partner when he/she is correct.**

2 **Your teacher will give you two Picasso's paints pages.**
Read the instructions and play the game.

1 Mark one Picasso's paints page *Send* and the other *Receive*.

2 Now work in pairs. Draw seven things from exercise 1 in the seven circles of paint on your *Send* page. DON'T show your *Send* page to your partner.

3 Take it in turns to guess what is in the different paints on your partner's *Send* page. Use the dialogue to help you.
   A: *Is there a cap in your red paint?*
   B: *No there isn't. Is there a cap in your red paint?*
   A: *Yes, there is.*

4 Complete your *Receive* page with your partner's answers. Draw what you hear in the different paints. Who can guess and draw all the words on his/her partner's palette correctly first?

5 When you finish, compare your *Send* and *Receive* pages. Could you send and receive all the words correctly? If not, practise saying the problem words in exercise 1 again.

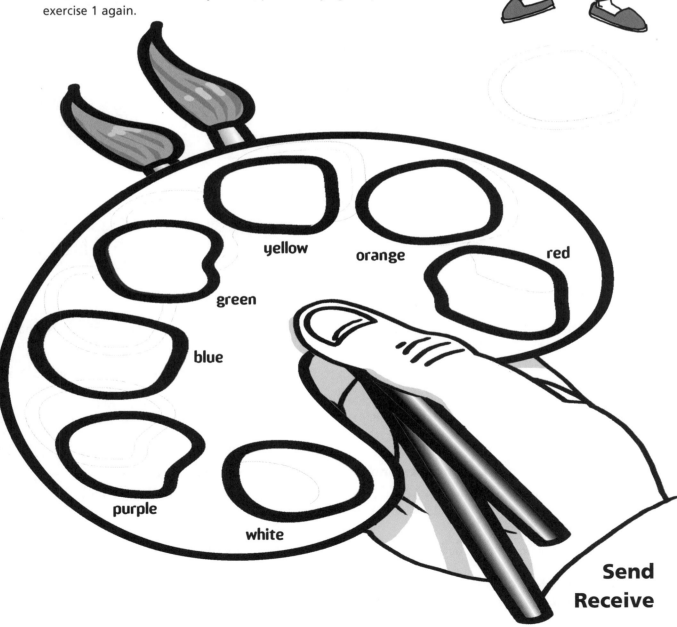

yellow   orange   red

green

blue

purple

white

Send
Receive

Street map dictation

1 Listen to the pairs of words. In the words on the left the first sound is /v/. In the words on the right the first sound is /w/. Can you hear the difference?

1 /v/ veils	2 /w/ Wales	3 /v/ veal	4 /w/ wheel
5 /v/ vest	6 /w/ west	7 /v/ vine	8 /w/ wine
9 /v/ V	10 /w/ we	11 /v/ vet	12 /w/ wet

2 **Read the instructions and practise saying the pairs of words in exercise 1.**

1 /v/ is a voiced consonant. Bite your bottom lip with your top teeth and push air out to make this sound.

2 /w/ is a short form of the long vowel sound /u:/. Put a pencil in your mouth and put your lips round it. Take the pencil out and keep your lips round. Push air out to make this sound.

3 Listen to the sentences. Then tick the correct answer, a or b, each time.

1 Do you like **veils / Wales**?
   a No, but I like hats. ☐
   b No, but I like Scotland. ☐

2 Tell me about that **vine / wine**.
   a We planted it in the garden last year. ☐
   b It's cold, white, sweet and German. ☐

3 Is this your **veal / wheel**?
   a No. I'm having fish. ☐
   b No. It's for Kate's car. ☐

4 Are you interested in the **vest / west**?
   a No, I want to buy a shirt. ☐
   b No, in the east. I love Asia. ☐

5 You're not listening. I said 'vet' / 'wet'.
   a Oh, I thought you said she was a doctor. ☐
   b Oh, I thought you said it was cold, but dry. ☐

6 I can't read your writing - is this 'V' / 'we'?
   a No, it's 'U'. ☐
   b No, it's 'me'. ☐

4 **Work in pairs. Take turns to start different dialogues from exercise 3. Your partner must listen and reply each time. Tell your partner when he/she is correct.**

5 Listen to these silly sentences and practise reading them aloud.

1 We want some lovely winter weather!

2 Why was Victor visiting Wanda on Wednesday?

3 Will's Venezuelan waistcoat was wonderful.

4 Wally won't wash Vinnie the whale.

5 Vera loves videoing Wayne on Valentine's day.

6 Vanessa and Val revised very well last weekend.

6 **Look at the street map of Letterton. Read the instructions and play the game.**

1 Work in pairs. One of you is Student A, the other is Student B.
Student A: Anna, Bob, Cathy, Donna, Eric, and Frank live in flats. Put the first letters of their names where you want in the numbered flats (the circles) on the map. (Write only one letter in each place!) DON'T show your map to your partner.
Student B: Gary, Harry, Izzy, Jessy, Keith, and Lily live in houses. Put the first letters of their names where you want in the numbered houses (the squares) on the map. (Write only one letter in each place!) DON'T show your map to your partner.

2 Get together with your partner.
Student A: You must find the houses where Gary, Harry, Izzy, Jessie, Kevin and Lily live.
Student B: You must find the flats where Anna, Bob, Cathy, and Donna, Eric and Frank live.

3 Take it is turns to ask and answer about your Letterton Street maps. Use the dialogue to help you.
A: *Where does Gary live?*
B: *In a house on the corner of West Avenue and Wales Road. Where does Anna live?*
A: *In a flat on the corner of Veils Road and Veedon Way.*

4 Complete your map with your partner's answers. Write the letters in the correct flats or houses.

5 When you finish, compare your maps. Could you send and receive all the addresses correctly? If not, practise the problem words in exercise 1 again.

Street map of Letterton

Veils Road

Weedon Way

West Avenue

Veal Street

Vest Avenue

Veedon Way

Vine Lane

Whales Road

Wheel Street

Wine Lane

KEY ◯ = FLATS ▢ = HOUSES

Find Pharoah's jewels

1 🎧²⁄₁₅ **Listen to these trios of words. In the words on the left the final sound is /n/. In the words in the middle the final sound is /ŋ/. In the words on the right the final sound is /ŋk/. Can you hear the difference?**

1 /n/ sun	**2** /ŋ/ sung	**3** /ŋk/ sunk
4 /n/ ban	**5** /ŋ/ bang	**6** /ŋk/ bank
7 /n/ ran	**8** /ŋ/ rang	**9** /ŋk/ rank
10 /n/ win	**11** /ŋ/ wing	**12** /ŋk/ wink
13 /n/ thin	**14** /ŋ/ thing	**15** /ŋk/ think

2 **Read the instructions and practise saying the trios of words in exercise 1.**

1 Put your tongue up to touch the top of your mouth and push air through your nose to make the sound /n/.

2 Put your tongue back as if you are going to make the sound /k/. With your tongue in this position try to say /n/. The sound that comes out will be /ŋ/.

3 First make the sound /ŋ/, then add /k/ at the end. This is the sound /ŋk/.

3 🎧 2/16 **Listen to the words and circle the correct pictures.**

4 **Work in pairs. Take turns to say different words from exercise 1. Your partner must listen and point to the correct picture each time. Tell your partner when he/she is correct.**

5 **Your teacher will give you two Dead Pharaoh Grid pages. Read the instructions and play the game.**

1 Mark one of the Dead Pharaoh grids *Send* and the other *Receive*.

2 You have eight jewels to put in the coffin, on the body or next to it. Draw them where you want on your *Send* page.
   Your jewels look like this on the picture. ◇ = ◈

3 Work in pairs. DON'T show your *Send* page to your partner. You must find your partner's jewels. Take it in turns to say the co-ordinates (word and number) for different squares on the grid. For example, *ban 3* = the square in the 2nd row and 3rd column. Use the dialogue to help you.
   A: *Is there a jewel in sun 8?*
   B: *Sun 8? Yes, there is. Is there a jewel in sun 6?*
   A: *Sun 6? No, there isn't.*

4 Complete your *Receive* page with your partner's answers. Mark the correct squares with a X or a O.
   X = there is a jewel on this square
   O = there is nothing on this square
   Who can be first to find all their partner's jewels?

5 When you finish, compare your *Send* and *Receive* pages. Could you send and receive all the co-ordinates correctly? If not, practise saying the problem words in exercise 1 again.

1 2 3 4 5 6 7 8 9 10 11 12

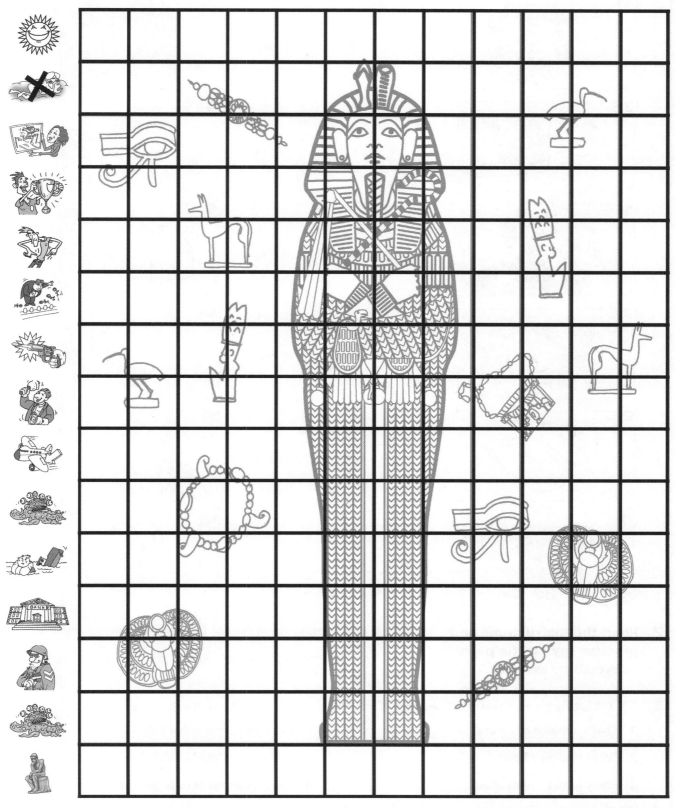

Send   Receive

Monster maze

1 Listen to these pairs of words. In the words on the left the first sound is a vowel. In the words on the right the first sound is /h/. Can you hear the difference?

1

no h **owl**   /h/ **howl**

2

3

no h **air**   /h/ **hair**

4

5

no h **eat**   /h/ **heat**

6

7

no h **eels**   /h/ **heels**

8

9

no h **eye**   /h/ **high**

10 7,230 METRES

11

no h **art**   /h/ **heart**

12

2 **Read the instructions and practise saying the pairs of words in exercise 1.**

1 There is no /h/ sound at the start of the words beginning with a vowel.

2 /h/ is a voiceless consonant. Open your mouth and push air out to make this sound.

3 Listen to the pairs of words. Circle the word you hear each time.

1 That's a loud **owl** / **howl**.

2 What nice **air** / **hair**!

3 Can you **eat** / **heat** it up?

4 I've never liked **eels** / **heels**.

5 Did you say 'eye' / 'high'?

6 She's a famous **art** / **heart** specialist.

4 **Work in pairs. Take turns to say different words from exercise 1. Your partner must listen and say *without 'h'* or *with 'h'* each time. Tell your partner when he/she is correct.**

5 Help the hero Theseus go through the maze and find the monster he must fight. Listen and follow the directions. Mark the route on the map. Which monster does he meet?

A Gorgon, The Minotaur, The Sphinx, a Basilisk, a Cyclops and a Harpy are waiting in the maze. A Centaur, a Triton, a Manticore, a Furia, a Gryphon and Cerberus are there, too. Are you ready?

Theseus

The Minotaur

The Sphinx

a Basilisk

a **a Cyclops**

b **a Harpy**

c **Cerberus**

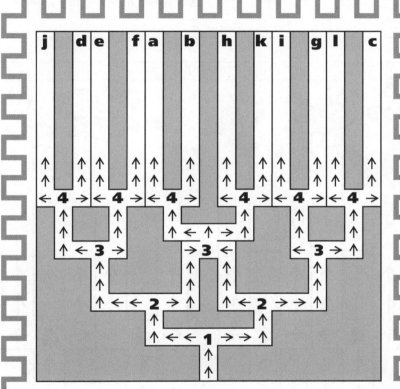

g **a Furia**

h **a Centaur**

i **a Manticore**

j **a Gorgon**

6 Your teacher will give you a Monster Maze. Read the instructions and play the game.

1 Work in pairs. Choose 4 magic words from exercise 1. Write them below. DON'T show your partner your Magic Word List.

2 Decide which monster you are sending your partner to meet. Write its name below, but DON'T show your partner.

3 Take it in turns to give Monster Maze directions, using your 4 magic words. Listen and mark the route your partner tells you.

4 When you finish, compare your Monster Mazes and Magic Words. Could you send and receive the instructions correctly? If not, practise saying the words in exercise 1 again.

k **a Triton**

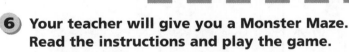

l **a Gryphon**

Magic Words:

1 ....

2 ....

3 ....

4 ....

The monster:

....

1   Walk into the maze. Go to point 1. Listen to the magic word. If you hear a vowel at the beginning go left, if you hear an 'h' at the beginning go right.
(Say your Magic Word 1)

2   Now go to point 2 in front of you. Listen to the magic word. If you hear a vowel at the beginning go left, if you hear an 'h' at the beginning go right.
(Say your Magic Word 2)

3   Now go to point 3 in front of you. Listen to the magic word. If you hear a vowel at the beginning go left, if you hear an 'h' at the beginning go right.
(Say your Magic Word 3)

4   Now go to point 4 in front of you. Listen to the magic word. If you hear a vowel at the beginning go left, if you hear an 'h' at the beginning go right.
(Say your Magic Word 4)

5   Which monster do you meet?

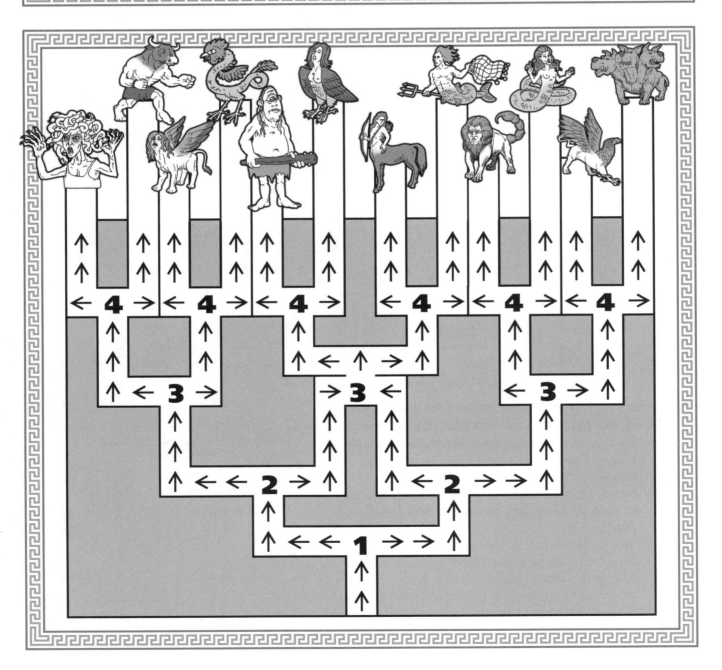

Get the goblins

1  Listen to these trios of words. In the words in column 1 the first sound is /j/. In the words in column 2 the first sound is /dʒ/. In the words in column 3 the first sound is /tʃ/. Can you hear the difference?

1 /j/ yolk
2 /dʒ/ joke
3 /tʃ/ choke
4 /j/ yes
5 /dʒ/ Jess
6 /tʃ/ chess
7 /j/ yin
8 /dʒ/ gin
9 /tʃ/ chin
10 /j/ years
11 /dʒ/ jeers
12 /tʃ/ cheers
13 /j/ use
14 /dʒ/ Jews
15 /tʃ/ choose

2 **Read the instructions and practise saying the trios of words in exercise 1.**

Magic Mirror

Princess Ella

The Goblins

1 Spread your lips to make the sound /iː/. With your mouth in this position make a short sound at the start of each word. (Don't touch the top of your mouth with your tongue!) This is the sound /j/.

2 /dʒ/ is a short voiced consonant. First make the sound /d/. Then add the sound /ʒ/ as in 'television'.

3 /tʃ/ is a short voiceless consonant. First make the sound /t/. Then add the sound /ʃ/ as in 'she'.

3 🎧 2/21 **Listen and circle the word you hear each time.**

1 yolk / joke / choke

2 yes / Jess / chess

3 yin / gin / chin

4 years / jeers / cheers

5 use / Jews / choose

4 **Work in pairs. Take turns to say different words from exercise 1. Your partner must listen and point to the picture each time. Tell your partner when he/she is correct.**

5 **Your teacher will give you two Elf Palace Map pages. Read the instructions and play the game.**

1 Mark one of the Elf Palace Map pages *Send* and the other *Receive*. Some goblins want to kidnap Ella the Elf Princess from her Palace. They have cloaks that make them invisible, but Ella can see them in her magic mirror.

2 You have 7 goblins. Draw them where you want on your *Send* page. Your goblins look like this on the map.

3 Now work in pairs. DON'T show your *Send* page to your partner. You must find your partner's goblins. Take it is turns to say the co-ordinates (word and number) for different squares on the map. For example, *years 6* = the square in the 4th row and 6th column.

When your partner says a square where there is a goblin, you must say *Hit!* When your partner says

a square where there is no goblin, you must say *Miss!* Use the dialogue to help you.

A: *Is there a goblin in yolk 18.*

B: *Yolk 18? Hit! Is there a goblin in gin 7?*

A: *Gin 7? No, there isn't. Miss!*

4 Complete your *Receive* page with your partner's answers. Mark the correct squares with a *X* or a *O*.
X = there is a dead goblin on this square
O = there is nothing on this square
Who can be first to get all their partner's goblins?

5 When you finish, compare your *Send* and *Receive* pages. Could you send and receive all the co-ordinates correctly? If not, practise saying the problem words in exercise 1 again.

Elf Palace Map

1 2 3 4 5 6 7 8 9 10 11 12 13 14 15 16 17 18

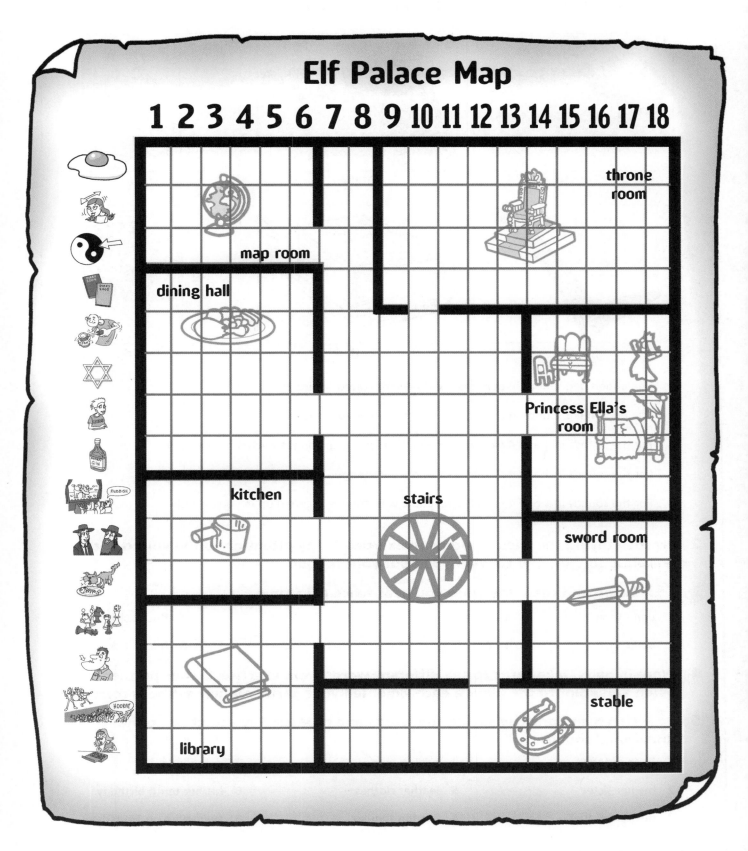

throne room

map room

dining hall

Princess Ella's room

kitchen

stairs

sword room

stable

library

Send   Receive

Thought bubble dictation

1 🎧 **Listen to the trios of words and circle the correct answers.**

/d/ <u>d</u>en

/ð/ <u>th</u>en

/z/ <u>Z</u>en

/t/ <u>t</u>ick

/θ/ <u>th</u>ick

/s/ <u>s</u>ick

1 The underlined sounds in <u>d</u>en, <u>th</u>en and <u>Z</u>en are **voiced** / **voiceless**.

2 The underlined sounds in <u>t</u>ick, <u>th</u>ick and <u>s</u>ick are **voiced** / **voiceless**.

3 For the sounds in **1 and 4 / 2 and 5 / 3 and 6** you put your tongue between your teeth.

4 For the sounds in **1 and 4 / 2 and 5 / 3 and 6** your tongue touches the top of your mouth.

5 For the sounds in **1 and 4 / 2 and 5 / 3 and 6** your tongue is curled up in your mouth.

2 **Practise saying the trios of words in exercise 1. Pay attention to the voiced and voiceless sounds, and to where you put your tongue.**

3 🎧 **Listen and circle the word you hear twice each time.**

1 den / then	**3** then / Zen	**5** tick / thick	**7** thick / sick
2 den / Zen	**4** Zen / den	**6** tick / sick	**8** thick / tick

4 **Work in pairs. Take turns to say different words from exercise 1. Your partner must listen and point to the picture each time. Tell your partner when he/she is correct.**

5 🎧 **Listen and practise saying the words and phrases. Pay attention to the underlined sounds.**

1 hi<u>s</u>/her <u>d</u>og	**4** having <u>d</u>inner	**7** <u>d</u>oing <u>j</u>udo
2 hi<u>s</u>/her <u>s</u>i<u>st</u>er	**5** lea<u>th</u>er clo<u>th</u>es	**8** hi<u>s</u>/her ten<u>th</u> bir<u>thd</u>ay
3 hi<u>s</u>/her bro<u>th</u>er	**6** getting <u>th</u>inner	**9** <u>s</u>wimming on <u>Th</u>ur<u>sd</u>ay

6 **Your teacher will give you two Thought Bubble Grid pages. Listen and practise saying the names from the grid.**

1   Mark one of the Thought bubble dictation grids *Send* and the other *Receive*.

2   On your *Send* page write the nine phrases from exercise 5 in the nine thought bubbles. Put one phrase in each bubble.

3   Now work in groups of three with two speakers (A and B) and one sound police officer (C). DON'T show your *Send* page to your speaking partner. Ask and answer about your Thought bubble dictation grids. Use the dialogue to help you.
    A: What's Cathy thinking about in your grid?
    B: 'her brother'. What's Cathy thinking about in your grid?
    A: 'having dinner'. What have you got in Zack's thought bubble?
    B: 'swimming on Thursday'. What have you got in Zack's thought bubble?

4   Complete your *Receive* page with your speaking partner's answers. Write the words in the correct shapes.

5   Student C is the Sound Police Officer. Listen to your classmates carefully. Every time one of your classmates says one of the six sounds correctly, you put a tick next to his or her name in the table. The sounds are: /d/,/ð/, /z/, /t/, /θ/, /s/.

6   When you finish, check with the Sound Police Officer. Who said most of the sounds correctly? If you made mistakes, practise saying the problem words in exercise 1 again.

7   Play the game again with a different person as the Sound Police Officer.

1 /θ/ Cathy

2 /t/ Peter

3 /ð/ Heather

4 /s/ Sue

5 /d/ Edward

6 /z/ Zach

7 /t/ Tanya

8 /z/ Louise

9 /θ/ Judith

Sound Police Officer's Table:

Student	Name	Correct sounds (total = ….)
A		
B		

Send
Receive

Number fun

1 (2/26) **Listen to these pairs of numbers and complete the stress rules (1-2) below.**

1	thirty	thirteen	**5**	seventy	seventeen
2	forty	fourteen	**6**	eighty	eighteen
3	fifty	fifteen	**7**	ninety	nineteen
4	sixty	sixteen			

1 The stress in *-ty* numbers is usually **Oo / oO**.

2 The stress in *-teen* numbers is usually **Oo / oO**.

2 (2/27) **Listen to the sentences and circle the numbers you hear.**

1 Bob Brown lives at number **90 / 19** Hill Road.

2 Today Emily Jones is **80 / 18**.

3 Let's meet at **4.50 / 4.15**.

4 What's the answer to question **30 / 13**?

5 And the winning ticket is blue number **60 / 16**.

6 That's **£3.40 / £3.14**.

7 My lucky number is **70 / 17**.

8 You're in room **30 / 13**.

3 **Work in pairs. Take it in turns to say the sentences in exercise 2 aloud, choosing one of the numbers. Listen and point each time to the numbers you hear. Your partner must say if you are correct or not.**

4 (2/28) **Listen to sentences 1-5 and complete the stress rule.**

1 That's seventeen euros, please.
2 There were thirteen people at the party.
3 Wait a minute...eighteen, nineteen, twenty!
4 Is that house number fifteen or sixteen?
5 He's fourteen years old.

> When we count, compare, or put a noun after a *-teen* number, the stress in the *-teen* number is **oO / Oo**.

5 **Listen and practise saying the sentences in exercise 4. Pay attention to the stress of the *-teen* words.**

6 (2/29) **Listen to the numbers. Colour the shapes in puzzle A of the numbers that you hear. What other number do the coloured shapes show?**

7 **Read the instructions and complete puzzle B.**

1 Work out the *-ty* and *-teen* numbered shapes that make another number in the puzzle. Write them down in a list.

2 Work in pairs. Student A: Dictate the numbers on your list to student B. Student B: Colour the shapes in puzzle B with the numbers you hear. What number does the puzzle show?

3 Then Student B dictates the numbers and A listens and colours the shapes in the puzzle. What number does the puzzle show?

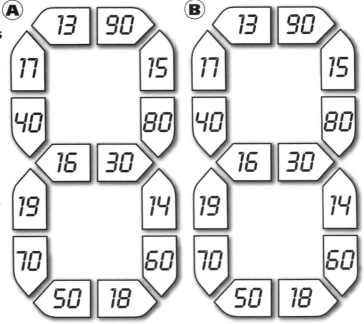

Can I present you with a present?

1 🔊 2/30 **Read the sentences and mark the underlined words V (verb) or N (noun). Then listen and pay attention to the stress in the underlined words.**

1 I am here to <u>present</u> the school prizes. ⬜

2 I got a lovely birthday <u>present</u> from Aunt Jane. ⬜

3 Many Arab countries <u>export</u> oil. ⬜

4 Whisky is an important Scottish <u>export</u>. ⬜

5 Can you <u>record</u> that programme for me? ⬜

6 He broke the 100 metres world <u>record</u> last year. ⬜

7 Don't <u>desert</u> me! I need you. ⬜

8 The Sahara <u>desert</u> is in North Africa. ⬜

9 Please don't <u>refuse</u> my help. ⬜

10 There's a bin for <u>refuse</u> outside the door. ⬜

11 I <u>object</u>! I really can't agree with this plan. ⬜

12 That's a strange <u>object</u>. What is it? ⬜

2 **Complete the stress rules.**

1 In two syllable verbs the stress is usually **Oo / oO**.   **2** In two syllable nouns the stress is usually **Oo / oO**.

3 **Practise saying the sentences in exercise 1 with the correct stress on the underlined words.**

4 🔊 2/31 **Listen to these words and mark them V (verb) or N (noun), depending on the stress.**

1 record	**3** export	**5** object ....
2 desert	**4** present	**6** refuse ....

5 **Work in pairs. Take turns to say different words from exercise 4. Your partner must listen and say *noun* or *verb* each time. Tell your partner when he/she is correct.**

Steve Strong and Walter Weak (1)

1 🎧 **Listen to the dialogues. Pay attention to the underlined verbs.**

1 A: <u>Can</u> I see you at two?
B: Yes, you <u>can</u>.

2 C: <u>Has</u> he got a tattoo?
D: Yes, he <u>has</u>.

3 E: <u>Have</u> you dyed your hair blue?
F: Yes, I <u>have</u>.

4 G: <u>Does</u> he work at the zoo?
H: Yes, he <u>does</u>.

5 I: <u>Do</u> you hate having flu?
J: Yes, I <u>do.</u>

6 K: <u>Are</u> your friends coming too?
L: Yes, they <u>are</u>.

7 M: <u>Were</u> you waiting for Sue?
N: Yes, we <u>were</u>.

8 O: <u>Was</u> that phone call for you?
P: Yes, it <u>was</u>.

2 **Complete the rules.**

1 When verbs start a long sentence and do not have a stress they usually sound **weak / strong**.

2 When verbs end a short sentence and have a stress they usually sound **weak / strong**.

3 〔2/33〕 **Listen to the strong and weak form of the verbs. Practise saying them.**

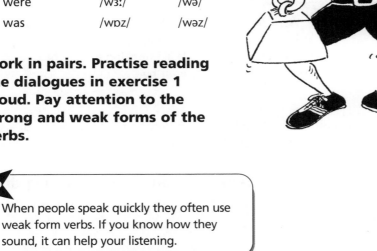

		strong	weak
1	can	/kæn/	/kən/
2	has	/hæz/	/həz/ or /əz/
3	have	/hæv/	/həv/ or /əv/
4	does	/dʌz/	/dəz/
5	do	/duː/	/də/
6	are	/ɑː/	/ə/
7	were	/wɜː/	/wə/
8	was	/wɒz/	/wəz/

4 **Work in pairs. Practise reading the dialogues in exercise 1 aloud. Pay attention to the strong and weak forms of the verbs.**

TIP

When people speak quickly they often use weak form verbs. If you know how they sound, it can help your listening.

5 〔2/34〕 **Verbs often sound weak in the middle of sentences, too. You will hear each sentence twice, once with a strong verb and once with a weak verb. Listen and complete the table with *strong* or *weak*.**

		1st time	2nd time
1	What <u>can</u> I do?	*strong*	*weak*
2	Why <u>has</u> it happened?	....	....
3	What <u>have</u> you done?	....	....
4	How <u>does</u> it work?	....	....
5	Where <u>do</u> you live?	....	....
6	What <u>are</u> you saying?	....	....
7	Where <u>were</u> you last night?	....	....
8	What <u>was</u> his name?	....	....

TIP

If you use strong form verbs when you speak, it will slow you down, and people may think you are rude or feeling angry. We use strong verb forms when we want to emphasise words.

6 **Work in pairs. Take turns to read a sentence from exercise 5 aloud, sometimes with a strong verb, sometimes with a weak verb. Listen to your partner and say each time *strong* or *weak*.**

Steve Strong and Walter Weak (2)

1 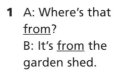 **Listen to the dialogues. Pay attention to the underlined prepositions.**

1 A: Where's that <u>from</u>?
B: It's <u>from</u> the garden shed.

2 C: What's that made <u>of</u>?
D: It's made <u>of</u> bread.

3 E: Who did you talk <u>to</u>?
F: I talked <u>to</u> Fred.

4 G: What are you looking <u>at</u>?
H: I'm looking <u>at</u> your bed.

5 I: What's that <u>for</u>?
J: It's <u>for</u> my head.

2 **Complete the rules.**

1 When prepositions come at the end of a question and have a stress they usually sound **weak / strong**.

2 When prepositions come in the middle of a sentence and do not have a stress they usually sound **weak / strong**.

3 **Listen to the strong and weak form of the prepositions. Practise saying them.**

		strong	**weak**				**strong**	**weak**
1	from	/frɒm/	/frəm/		**4**	at	/æt/	/ət/
2	of	/ɒv/	/əv/		**5**	for	/fɔː/	/fə/ or /fər/
3	to	/tuː/	/tə/					

4 **Work in pairs. Practise reading the dialogues in exercise 1 aloud. Pay attention to the strong and weak pronunciation of the prepositions.**

TIP

When people speak quickly they often use weak form prepositions. If you know how they sound, it can help your listening.

5 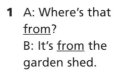 **Listen to the sentences. Pay attention to the weak form of the prepositions.**

6 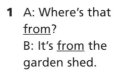 **Now listen to some foreign students saying the same sentences. Do they pronounce the prepositions correctly with weak forms? Mark them correct or incorrect.**

TIP

If you use strong form prepositions in the middle of sentences when you speak, it will slow you down.

		Correct	Incorrect
			✔
1	He's from Greece.	....	....
2	He's the president of France.	....	....
3	It's ten to nine.	....	....
4	Let's meet at my house.	....	....
5	Is that for Anna?	....	....
6	Do you come from Poland?	....	....
7	Did you speak to your teacher?	....	....
8	Are you here for the summer?	....	....

7 **Work in pairs. Take turns to read a sentence from exercise 6 aloud. Listen and say each time if the pronunciation of the preposition is correct.**

Are you free tonight?

1 🔊 2/39 **Listen to the conversation between Calvin the cave boy and Carla the cave girl. One of the sounds they use /ə/ is called 'schwa'. Schwa is a very common sound in English. It is underlined in the dialogue.**

> Are y<u>ou</u> free <u>a</u>t nine <u>o</u>'clock t<u>o</u>night?

> Look! Don't both<u>er</u> me! Please go <u>a</u>way!

2 🔊 2/40 **Listen to these sentences. Pay attention to the stressed words and the underlined words with the weak vowel sound schwa /ə/.**

1 I've got <u>an</u> appointm<u>e</u>nt <u>a</u>t th<u>e</u> hairdress<u>er</u>'s <u>a</u>t ten.

2 I'm meeting Sue f<u>or</u> coffee <u>a</u>t elev<u>en</u>

3 I'm going f<u>or</u> lunch with Aunt Jane <u>a</u>t one.

4 I'm going t<u>o</u> th<u>e</u> swimming pool with Joe <u>a</u>t three.

5 I'm seeing th<u>e</u> dentist <u>a</u>t seven f<u>or</u> <u>a</u> check up.

3 **Match up the sentence halves to make rules for sentence stress and schwa in sentences.**

1 Content words (giving important information in a sentence like *what? where? when? who? why?*)

2 Words like articles and prepositions (which don't give important information in a sentence)

3 Content words with more than one syllable

a can have the sound /ə/ in them on unstressed syllables.

b are stressed.

c are often pronounced with the sound /ə/ when people speak quickly.

4 **Say the sentences in exercise 2. Pay attention to the stresses and the schwas.**

5 🔊 2/41 **Listen to the sentences. Mark the stresses like this ◡ . Underline the schwa sounds.**

1 He's staying <u>at</u> home tonight t<u>o</u> revise f<u>or</u> th<u>e</u> test tomorrow.

2 She's going skating with Peter this Saturday.

3 We're meeting at nine o'clock in front of the cinema.

4 They're having a party at their house on Friday.

5 I'm away on holiday from the first to the fifteenth of August.

6 **Practise saying the sentences in exercise 5 aloud. Pay attention to the stresses and the schwas.**

The rhythm of the band

1 (2/42) **Listen to the poem and mark the stresses.**

Old Mr Sand is a one-man band.

You hear him everywhere.

Use the word stress of each instrument

To match it with its pair.

2 **Complete the sentences about the poem below.**

1 Lines 1 and 3 have **three / four** sentence stresses (or 'beats').
2 Lines 2 and 4 have **three / four** sentence stresses (or 'beats').

3 **Say the poem in exercise 1 aloud rhythmically. Clap your hands or snap your fingers on the beats.**

4 (2/43) (2/44) **Listen to the names of Mr Sand's instruments and put them in the correct place in the table according to the word stress. Then listen and check your answers.**

Word stress	Instrument 1	Instrument 2
O	....	....
Oo	....	....
oO	*guitar*	....
Ooo	....	....
oOo	....	....
ooO	....	....
oOoo	....	....

1 guitar

2 cymbals

3 drum

4 flute

5 accordion

6 harmonica

7 maracas

8 piano

9 saxophone

10 tambourine

11 triangle

12 trombone

13 trumpet

14 violin

5 (2/45) **Now listen and say the whole poem rhythmically with the instrument names.**

Old Mr Sand is a one-man band.
You hear him everywhere.
Use the word stress of each instrument
To match it with its pair.
O and *O*.
Oo go with *Oo*.
oO is like *oO*.

Ooo matches with *Ooo*.
oOo are paired with *oOo*.
ooO has its pair *ooO*.
oOoo together with *oOoo*.
That's the rhythm of the band.
Clap or snap it with your hand.
The rhythm of the one-man band.

Internet café

1 **2 46** **Ian the Internet café waiter is checking the email addresses of his friends in the café. He made lots of mistakes when he wrote them earlier. Listen and underline the stress on the email addresses where his friends correct him.**

1 kasia.popko@fastfrog.pl

2 theo.prodromou@mailbird.gr

3 helga.kaufmann@surfercat.at

4 dieter.braun@digimouse.de

5 joelle.dubois@ webchicken.fr

6 fabio.fonzo@cyberdog.it

2 **Read the rules and play the game.**

1   Work in groups and sit in a circle round a desk. On a piece of paper invent an email address for yourself.

2   Keep a copy of your address and pass the piece of paper to your right.

3   On the new piece of paper in front of you write a completely false email address above the real one.

4   Now ask the person on your left their email address using one false part.

5   Your partner must correct you putting the stress in the right place on their real address.

6   Take it in turns to answer the person on your right and ask the person on your left. Change the false piece of the address using corrective stress each time.

john.bull@superbull.uk

fred.smith@fastfrog.us
john.bull@superbull.uk

Is your email address john.bull@superfrog.uk?

No, it's john.bull@superbull.uk

Tasteless Terry

1 (2/47) **Listen to the three sentences. Pay attention to the tune - or 'intonation' - each time. Where does the voice go up?** ⟋ **Where does it go down?** ⟍ **Choose the correct intonation pattern each time.**

1   **a** I'd like a shirt, please.   ☐

   b I'd like a shirt, please.   ☐

2   **a** I'd like a shirt and a tie, please.   ☐

   b I'd like a shirt and a tie, please.   ☐

3   **a** I'd like a shirt, a tie and a jacket, please.   ☐

   b I'd like a shirt, a tie and a jacket, please.   ☐

2 **Complete the list intonation rule.**

When we list things the intonation goes **up / down** on the last thing in the list but **up / down** on all the things before the last.

3 **Listen and say the sentences in exercise 1. Pay attention to the intonation.**

4 (2/48) **Listen to some people playing the Tasteless Terry game. Mark the correct intonation over the underlined words.**

Student 1:   Tasteless Terry's wearing a red <u>shirt</u>.

Student 2:   Tasteless Terry's wearing a red <u>shirt</u> and a green <u>tie</u>.

Student 3:   Tasteless Terry's wearing a red <u>shirt</u>, a green <u>tie</u> and a brown <u>jacket</u>.

Student 4:   Tasteless Terry's wearing a red <u>shirt</u>, a green <u>tie</u>, a brown <u>jacket</u> and purple <u>jeans</u>.

Student 5:   Tasteless Terry's wearing a red <u>shirt</u>, a green <u>tie</u>, a brown <u>jacket</u>, purple <u>jeans</u> and pink <u>trainers</u>.

5 **Listen and say the sentences in exercise 4. Pay attention to the intonation.**

6 🎧 **2/49** **Listen and repeat the words.**

black   blue   brown   green   grey   orange   pink   purple   red   white   yellow

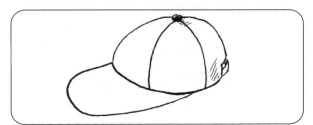

cap

hat

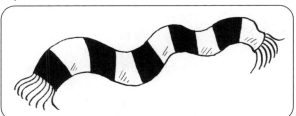

scarf

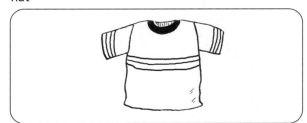

T-shirt

shorts

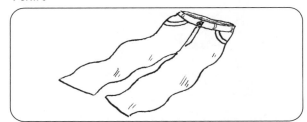

trousers

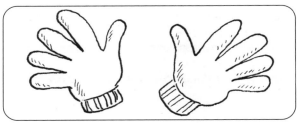

gloves

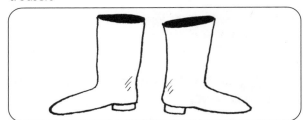

boots

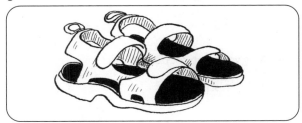

sandals

socks

7 **Work in groups. Read the rules and then use the words in exercise 6 to play the Tasteless Terry game. Pay attention to the intonation.**

1 Student 1 says a sentence similar to the first sentence in exercise 4.

2 Student 2 repeats the sentence and adds a new piece of clothing.

3 Continue round the group taking it in turns to add a new piece of clothing at the end of the sentence. What's the longest sentence you can remember?

4 Repeat the game. This time, students who forget or make a mistake are out of the game. The winner is the student who doesn't forget or make a mistake.

Job hunting

1 Listen to the phone conversation. Pay attention to the intonation in the questions and the answers.

Harry: Hello. Can I help you?

Steve: Yes. Is that Henderson's Holiday Camp?

Harry: Yes, it is. Are you ringing about the job advertisement?

Steve: Yes, I am. I'm Steve Somerville by the way.

Harry: Right, Steve, and I'm Harry Henderson. Have you got any relevant experience?

Steve: Yes, I have. I worked washing dishes in my uncle's restaurant last summer.

Harry: Good. That sounds perfect. Can you come for an interview today?

Steve: Yes, I can. Is that at 10 Green Street?

Harry: That's right. Shall we say at three o'clock?

Steve: Yes. Thanks. Goodbye, Mr Henderson.

Harry: Goodbye.

SUMMER JOB
washing dishes at Henderson's Holiday Camp. Good wages. Ring **982 423 998**. Head Office: 10 Green Street

2 Complete the intonation rules.

1 In *Yes/No* questions the intonation goes **up** / **down** at the end.

2 In statements the intonation goes **up** / **down** at the end.

3 Listen to the mini-dialogues and mark the intonation on the questions and the statements.

1 A: Are you here for the summer job?

B: Yes, I am.

2 A: Please come in.

B: Thank you.

3 B: Am I late?

A: Was your appointment for three?

4 A: Do sit down.

B: Thanks.

5 A: Did you phone earlier?

B: Yes, I did.

6 A: Is your name Eric Everton?

B No, it isn't.

7 A: I'm Steve Somerville.

B: Is that S-O-M-E-R-V-I-L-L-E?

8 A: Can you start next week?

B: Yes, of course.

4 Work in pairs. Read the mini-dialogues in exercise 3 aloud paying attention to the intonation.

High Street shopping

1 🎧 **2/52** **Listen to the intonation in the questions.**

A *Wh*- questions
1 Where are you?
2 What have you bought?
3 Who's with you?
4 When are you coming home?

B *Yes/No* questions
5 Are you in the butcher's?
6 Have you bought some sausages?
7 Is Jenny with you?
8 Are you coming home at eleven o'clock?

2 **Complete the question intonation rules.**

1 In *Wh*- questions the intonation usually goes **up / down** at the end.

2 In *Yes/No* questions the intonation usually goes **up / down** at the end.

3 **Practise saying the questions in exercise 1 with the correct intonation.**

4 Imagine you are shopping and complete the Questionnaire. Don't show it to your classmates!

5 🎧 2/53 Listen and practise the dialogues with a partner. Pay attention to the question intonation.

Cathy:	Are you in the butcher's?
Peter:	Yes, I am.
Cathy:	Have you bought any sausages?
Peter:	Yes, I have.
Cathy:	Is Jenny with you?
Peter:	Yes, she is.
Cathy:	Is Billy with you?
Peter:	Yes, he is.
Cathy:	Are you coming home at eleven o'clock?
Peter:	Yes, I am.

Cathy:	Are you in the butcher's?
Nora:	No, I'm not.
Cathy:	Have you bought any sausages?
Nora:	No, I haven't.
Cathy:	Is Jenny with you?
Nora:	No, she isn't.
Cathy:	Is Billy with you?
Nora:	No, he isn't.
Cathy:	Are you coming home at eleven o'clock?
Nora:	No, I'm not.

SHOPPING QUESTIONNAIRE

BUTCHER'S   BAKER'S   CHEMIST'S   GREENGROCER'S

1 Which shop are you in now? (choose 1 answer)
☐ the butcher's   ☐ the baker's
☐ the chemist's   ☐ the greengrocer's

2 What have you bought? (choose 5 things)
☐ hamburgers   ☐ sausages
☐ bread   ☐ cakes
☐ cheese   ☐ biscuits
☐ carrots   ☐ potatoes
☐ toothpaste   ☐ shampoo

3 Who's with you? (choose 1 answer)
☐ Jenny   ☐ Tommy
☐ Billy   ☐ Rosie
☐ Sally

4 When are you coming home? (choose 1 answer)
☐ 11 o'clock   ☐ 12 o'clock
☐ 1 o'clock   ☐ 2 o'clock

6 Take it in turns to ask *Yes/No* questions to find out about your partner's Shopping Questionnaire information. Use the dialogues in exercise 5 to help you. Write the answers in the grid. Who can complete it first?

Where?	
What/bought? 1	
2	
3	
4	
5	
Who/with/you?	
When/coming home?	

7 Now change partners. Ask *Wh-* questions to find out quickly about your new partner's conversation with his/her previous partner. Pay attention to the *Wh-* question intonation.

1 Where was your partner? ....

2 What five things had he/she bought? ....

....

....

3 Who was with him/her? ....

4 When was he/she coming home? ....

Fred Sure and Rita Unsure

1 🎧 **2/54** **Fred is very sure of himself. He always knows the answer before he asks the question. Listen to these sentences. Pay attention to the tune - or 'intonation' - each time. Does Fred's voice go up or down at the end? Choose the correct intonation pattern.**

1 **a** You're from Poland, aren't you?   ↗ ☐
   b You're from Poland, aren't you?   ↘ ☐

2 **a** You name's Jacek, isn't it?   ↗ ☐
   b You name's Jacek, isn't it?   ↘ ☐

3 **a** You live in Warsaw, don't you?   ↗ ☐
   b You live in Warsaw, don't you?   ↘ ☐

2 **Listen and say the sentences in exercise 1. Pay attention to the intonation.**

3 🎧 **2/55** **Rita isn't very sure of herself. She never remembers things and often has to ask the same question many times. Listen to these sentences. Pay attention to the tune - or 'intonation' - each time. Does Rita's voice go up or down at the end? Choose the correct intonation pattern then practise saying the sentences.**

1 **a** You're from Poland, aren't you?   ↗ ☐
   b You're from Poland, aren't you?   ↘ ☐

2 **a** You name's Jacek, isn't it?   ↗ ☐
   b You name's Jacek, isn't it?   ↘ ☐

3 **a** You live in Warsaw, don't you?   ↗ ☐
   b You live in Warsaw, don't you?   ↘ ☐

4 **Complete the rules.**

1 When you are sure, the intonation goes **up / down** in the question tag. You simply want someone to agree with you.

2 When you aren't sure, the intonation goes **up / down** in the question tag. You are really asking a question.

5 🎧 **2/56** **Listen to some people saying question tag sentences. Mark the intonation *R* if it rises like Rita's, or *F* if it falls like Fred's.**

1 You like pizza, don't you?   ↗ ....R.......

2 You don't like fish, do you?   ....

3 You're 16, aren't you?   ....

4 You aren't ill, are you?   ....

5 You've got a motorbike, haven't you? ....

6 You haven't got a computer, have you? ....

7 You can swim, can't you?   ....

8 You can't speak French, can you?   ....

6 **Listen and practise the sentences in exercise 5. Pay attention to the intonation.**

7 **Work in pairs. Take it in turns to say a sentence from exercise 5. Take care with the intonation of the question tag. Your partner must listen to the intonation and say if you are sure or unsure.**

Polite Polly and Rude Rupert

1 🎧 (2/57) **Listen to the Polite Polly asking her parents to do things for her. Then listen to Rude Rupert asking his parents to do the same things for him.**

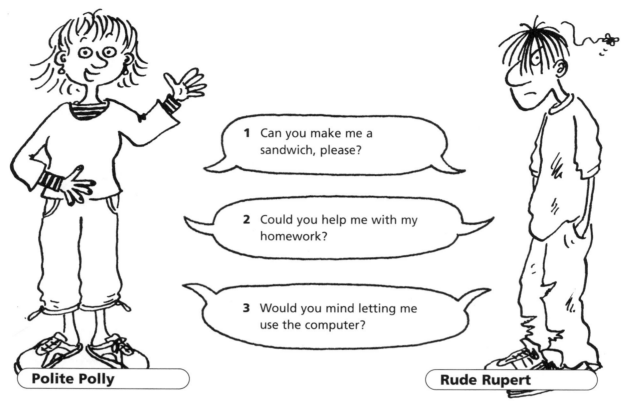

1 Can you make me a sandwich, please?

2 Could you help me with my homework?

3 Would you mind letting me use the computer?

Polite Polly

Rude Rupert

2 **Answer the questions.**

1 Do you think Polly's parents will be happy to help her?

a Yes, probably.   **b** No, probably not.

2 Do you think Rupert's parents will be happy to help him?

a Yes, probably.   **b** No, probably not.

3 **Complete the intonation and stress rules for polite and rude requests.**

1 If you start high, go down at the end, and don't put heavy stresses on all the words in a request, you will sound **polite and pleasant / rude and angry**

e.g. Could you open the window?

2 If you start low, go up at the end, and put heavy stresses on all the words in a request you will sound **polite and pleasant / rude and angry.**

e.g. Could you open the window?

4 🎧 (2/58) **Now listen to Mum and Dad asking Polly and Rupert to do things. Mark each request *P* (polite) or *R* (rude).**

1 Would you mind turning that radio down? ....R....   **5** Could you play with that ball outside? ....

2 Can you tidy your bedroom, please? ....   **6** Would you mind changing channels? ....

3 Could you get off the phone soon? ....   **7** Could you keep the noise down? ....

4 Can you clear the table, please? ....   **8** Would you mind closing your door? ....

5 **Work in pairs. Take turns to read a request from exercise 4 aloud. Listen and say each time if the intonation and stress sounds polite or rude.**

DVD collections

1 🎧 **2/59 When people speak quickly they link the consonant sound at the end of one word with the vowel sound at the start of the next word. Listen.**

Look_at my collection_of DVDs.

I'm looking at_it. It's_amazing!

2 🎧 **2/60 Listen and mark the links in these DVD titles.**

1 The Lord of the Rings
2 Twenty Thousand Leagues under the Sea
3 Gangs of New York
4 Charley's Angels
5 Artificial Intelligence
6 Wyatt Earp

3 🎧 **2/61 Listen to this dialogue and read the information.**

'I found this one in a second hand shop last week.

Really?

> Sometimes we don't pronounce the letters *t* or *d* when they come at the end of a word and the next word starts with a consonant sound.

4 🎧 **2/62 Listen and cross out the unpronounced *t* and *d* sounds in these film titles.**

1 The Lost World
2 Around the World in Eighty Days
3 Dr Jekyll and Mr Hyde
4 The Secret Garden
5 David Copperfield
6 The Last Samurai

5 🎧 **2/63 Listen to the dialogue and read the information.**

1 We add in a linking /j/ when the vowel /iː/ ends one word and the next word starts with a vowel sound. For example: The /j/ Exorcist
2 We add in a linking /w/ when a rounded vowel (/uː/ /əʊ/) ends one word and the next word starts with a vowel sound. For example: Romeo /w/ and Juliet.

The /j/ Exorcist is my favourite.

And mine's Romeo /w/ and Juliet.

6 🎧 **2/64 Listen and add linking /j/ and /w/ in these film titles.**

1 The Elephant Man
2 Catch Me If You Can
3 Much Ado About Nothing
4 Charlie and the Chocolate Factory
5 The Invisible Man
6 Mickey Blue Eyes

TIP
People will understand you if you don't use linking when you speak, but linking helps you to speak faster and more smoothly. It is very important to understand linking in order to improve your listening skills.

7 **Work in pairs. Take turns to read DVD titles from exercises 2, 4 and 6 aloud, sometimes with linking and sometimes with no linking. Listen and say each time if your partner is using linking or not.**

Have we run out of petrol?

1 **Match the meanings in the box with the phrasal verbs in bold in the sentences below.**

1 Have we **run out of** petrol?   *used all of the*
                                                     ....

2 You've **put off** the wedding again!   ....

3 They **get on with** each other very well.   ....

4 She **turned up** at four o'clock.   ....

5 I **came across** it in a jumble sale.   ....

6 He **goes in** for every competition.   ....

> arrived unexpectedly
> enters
> found
> like and agree with
> ~~used all of the~~
> postponed

2 **Match the sentences 1-6 in exercise 1 with the pictures (a-f).**

a

....

b

....

c

....

d

....

e

....

f

....

3 (2/65) **Read the information. Then listen and mark the links in the sentences in exercise 1.**

When people speak quickly, they link the consonant sound at the end of one word with the vowel sound at the start of the next word. For example: run‿out‿of.

4 **Match the meanings in the box with the phrasal verbs in bold in the sentences below.**

1 The number of students in each class **went down** last term. ....*fell*........

2 She **turned down** Andy's invitation. ....

3 They **called** the concert **off**. ....

4 The firemen **put** the fire **out**. ....

5 We **went through** some bad times last December! ....

6 He **made** the whole thing **up**. ....

> experienced
> ~~fell~~
> invented
> rejected
> cancelled
> extinguished

5 (2/66) **Read the information and then listen and cross out the unpronounced *t* and *d* sounds in the sentences in exercise 4.**

Sometimes we don't pronounce the letters *t* or *d* when they come at the end of a word and the next word starts with a consonant. For example: wen~~t~~ down

6 **Match the meanings in the box with the phrasal verbs in bold in the sentences below.**

1 Prices **go up** all the time. ....*rise*........

2 I **go away** to the countryside every weekend. ....

3 I **ran into** my uncle at the party. ....

4 Look! That boy on the motorbike's **getting away**! ....

5 I wouldn't **go into** the old library at night! ....

6 **Go on** trying and you'll do it in the end. ....

> disappear
> continue
> ~~rise~~
> met (by chance)
> enter
> escaping

7 (2/67) **Read the information and then listen and mark the extra /j/ and /w/ sounds in the sentences in exercise 6.**

1 We add in a linking /j/ when a spread vowel (/iː/ /i/ /ɔɪ/ /eɪ/ or /aɪ/) ends one word and the next word starts with a vowel sound. For example: away /j/ on holiday

2 We add in a linking /w/ when a rounded vowel (/uː/ or /əʊ/) ends one word and the next word starts with a vowel sound. For example: go /w/ up

★TIP
People will understand you if you don't use linking when you speak, but linking helps you to speak faster and more smoothly. It is very important to understand linking in order to improve your listening skills.

8 **Work in pairs. Take turns to read the sentences from exercises 1, 4 and 6 aloud, sometimes with linking and sometimes with no linking. Listen and say each time if your partner is using linking or not.**

Fred Formal and Ian Informal

1 🎧 2/68 **In formal speech and writing we don't use contractions. Listen and complete Fred Formal's speech.**

> **1** .... like to say thank you to the Mayor of Newton for inviting me today. **2** .... here of course to open this new museum. **3** .... visited many museums in my life and I **4** .... remember a better one. **5** .... with great pleasure therefore that I declare this museum open.

2 🎧 2/69 **In informal speech and writing we usually use contractions. Listen to Ian Informal's speech and write the contractions in the gaps below.**

> **1** .... like to say thanks to all my fans for coming to see me at the airport. **2** .... here to give a concert in London. **3** .... visited Britain once before, fifteen years ago, but I was very young and I **4** .... remember much about it. **5** .... going to be a great concert!

3 🎧 2/70 **Listen and write the sentences with contractions.**

1 You should not smoke. ....

2 There is a zoo near our town. ....

3 It will be ready tomorrow. ....

4 I did not like it. ....

5 Who is that? ....

6 Do not worry. ....

7 They had met years ago. ....

8 You must not panic. ....

9 Who would like ice cream? ....

10 She has not arrived yet. ....

TIP
People will understand you if you don't use contractions when you speak, but contractions help you to speak faster and more smoothly. It is very important to understand contractions in order to improve your listening skills.

4 **Work in pairs. Take turns to read sentences from exercise 3 aloud, sometimes with contractions and sometimes without contractions. Listen and say each time if your partner is using contractions or not.**

How many syllables?

1 🎧 **2/71** 'Syllables' are the parts of a word when you say it. The word **syll-a-ble**, for example, has got three parts. Read the information and then listen to the words. Can you hear the difference?

Americans usually pronounce all the syllables in long words.

Standard British English speakers often miss out a syllable to make long words shorter.

1 *Dictionary* has 4 syllables in American English.

2 *Dictionary* has 3 syllables in British English.

2 🎧 **2/72** **Listen to these words in British English. Cross out the silent syllables.**

1 uncomfortable	**3** medicine	**5** miserable	**7** restaurant	**9** mathematical
2 camera	**4** history	**6** mystery	**8** documentary	**10** literature

3 🎧 **2/73** **Listen to the words in exercise 2 in American English. Can you hear how all the syllables are sounded?**

4 🎧 **2/74** **Read and match the pictures with the sentences. Then listen and mark the pronunciation A (American) or B (British). Use the <u>underlined</u> words to help you decide.**

a
b
c
d
e

f
g
h
i
j

1	This jacket is very <u>uncomfortable</u>.	(A) B	**6**	She likes <u>mystery</u> stories.	A B
2	Is that my <u>camera</u>?	A B	**7**	What a lovely Polish <u>restaurant</u>!	A B
3	I'd like some cough <u>medicine</u>, please.	A B	**8**	This is a great <u>documentary</u>.	A B
4	He's studying French <u>history</u>.	A B	**9**	He was a <u>mathematical</u> genius.	A B
5	Don't be so <u>miserable</u>!	A B	**10**	I love Greek <u>literature</u>.	A B

5 **Work in pairs. Take turns to read a sentence from exercise 4 aloud, sometimes with American pronunciation and sometimes with British pronunciation. Listen to the syllables in the underlined word and say each time if your partner is using American or British English.**

Are you bored?

1 (2/75) **Americans often pronounce the letter *r* when in Standard British English it is silent. Listen to Amy and Brett saying these words. Can you hear the difference?**

> *I'm Brett. I'm from the United Kingdom.*

> *I'm Amy. I'm from the United States.*

1 fur
2 four
3 bored
4 card
5 thirsty
6 star

NOTE: Irish and Scottish speakers also use sounded *r*.

2 (2/76) **Listen to different people saying these words, once with silent *r* and once with sounded *r*. Mark the order you hear the words: 1 = first, 2 = second.**

	silent *r*	sounded *r*
1 fur		
2 four		
3 star		

	silent *r*	sounded *r*
4 bored		
5 card		
6 thirsty		

3 (2/77) **Listen to people saying these sentences. Mark them A (American) or B (British). Use the sound of *r* in the underlined words to decide.**

1 Is that a real fox <u>fur</u>? (A) B

2 Let's meet at <u>four</u>. A B

3 Look at that <u>star</u>! A B

4 He's <u>bored</u>. A B

5 I'd like some Christmas <u>cards</u>, please. A B

6 She's <u>thirsty</u>. A B

7 This is a fake <u>fur</u> coat. A B

8 She's an old Hollywood <u>star</u>. A B

9 This is my business <u>card</u>. A B

10 My nephew's <u>four</u> today. A B

4 **Work in pairs. Take turns to read a sentence from exercise 3 aloud, sometimes with sounded *r*, sometimes with silent *r*. Listen and say each time if your partner is using American or British pronunciation.**

5 (2/78) **In British English we sound the final *r* in a word when the next word in the sentence starts with a vowel sound (a, e, i, o, u). Listen to these silly sentences. Pay attention to the linking *r* sounds.**

1 Carla's here in Krakow for a fortnight.

2 Arthur English wants to buy four elephants.

3 Would you like a pear or a banana for elevenses?

4 Poor Uncle Fred has got sore ears.

5 My guitar is under Ernest's rubber octopus.

6 Dear Aunt Agatha, where are all your paper aeroplanes?

6 **Practise saying the silly sentences in exercise 5 aloud. Take care with the linking *r* sounds.**

I'm Australian?

1 (2/79) **Intonation is the 'music' of a sentence. There is rising intonation ⤴ and falling intonation ⤵. Listen to Alec and Belinda talking about intonation in Australia and Britain.**

In Australia we use rising intonation at the end of a statement.

In Britain we use falling intonation at the end of a statement.

2 (2/80) **Listen and mark the intonation in these sentences.**

1	I'm Alec.	⤵	⤴
2	I'm Australian.	⤵	⤴
3	I'm from Sydney.	⤵	⤴

4	I'm Belinda.	⤵	⤴
5	I'm British.	⤵	⤴
6	I'm from London.	⤵	⤴

NOTE: People from Wales also use rising intonation for statements.

3 (2/81) **Listen to these statements. Are the speakers British or Australian? Mark the intonation rising ⤴ or falling ⤵ to help you decide.**

	Australian	British			Australian	British
1 I'm sixteen.				**5** Frank's my brother.		
2 I'm a student.				**6** I'm on holiday here.		
3 I like swimming.				**7** Here's ten dollars.		
4 It's very hot today.				**8** They're waiting for us.		

4 **Work in pairs. Take turns to read a sentence from exercise 3 aloud, paying attention to the intonation at the end. Listen and say each time if your partner is using Australian or British intonation.**

5 (2/82) **Read the information and then listen and mark these sentences ? (question/surprise) or . (statement).**

Sometimes in modern British English, people use statement word order with rising intonation to ask a question or show surprise.

		Question/ Surprise	Statement
1	You're English		
2	He's a student		
3	She likes computers		
4	This is what's for dinner		
5	Gary's her boyfriend		
6	You're on holiday here		
7	That cost six euros		
8	They're arriving tomorrow		

6 **Work in pairs. Take turns to read a sentence from exercise 5 aloud, paying attention to the intonation at the end. Listen and say each time if your partner is asking a question/showing surprise or making a statement.**

'Elp me 'Arry

1 (2/83) **Read the information and then listen to Carl and Bella saying the words (1-8). Can you hear the difference?**

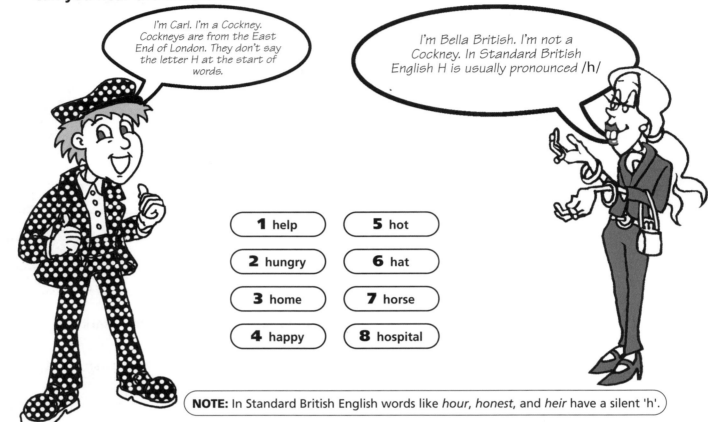

I'm Carl. I'm a Cockney. Cockneys are from the East End of London. They don't say the letter H at the start of words.

I'm Bella British. I'm not a Cockney. In Standard British English H is usually pronounced /h/

1 help	**5** hot
2 hungry	**6** hat
3 home	**7** horse
4 happy	**8** hospital

NOTE: In Standard British English words like *hour*, *honest*, and *heir* have a silent 'h'.

2 (2/84) **Listen to different people saying these words, once with /h/ and once without /h/. Mark the order you hear the words: 1 = first, 2 = second.**

	with /h/	without /h/
1 help	2	1
2 hungry		
3 home		
4 happy		

	with /h/	without /h/
5 hot		
6 hat		
7 horse		
8 hospital		

3 (2/85) **Listen to these sentences. Mark them C (Cockney) or SB (Standard British English). Use the pronunciation of *h* in the underlined words to decide.**

1 <u>Help</u> me, <u>Harry</u>!   C   SB

2 Are you <u>hungry</u>?   C   SB

3 <u>His</u> <u>home</u> is in <u>Helsinki</u>.   C   SB

4 I'm so <u>happy</u> in <u>Holland</u>.   C   SB

5 It's very <u>hot</u> in <u>here</u>.   C   SB

6 <u>Have</u> you got a new <u>hat</u>?   C   SB

7 <u>Horses</u> aren't <u>horrible</u>.   C   SB

8 <u>He's</u> in <u>hospital</u>.   C   SB

4 **Work in pairs. Take turns reading sentences from exercise 3 aloud, paying attention to the pronunciation of *h*. Listen and say each time if your partner is using Cockney or Standard British English pronunciation.**

What's dis?

1 (2/86) **Read the information and then listen to Jimmy and Emily saying the words (1-8). Can you hear the difference?**

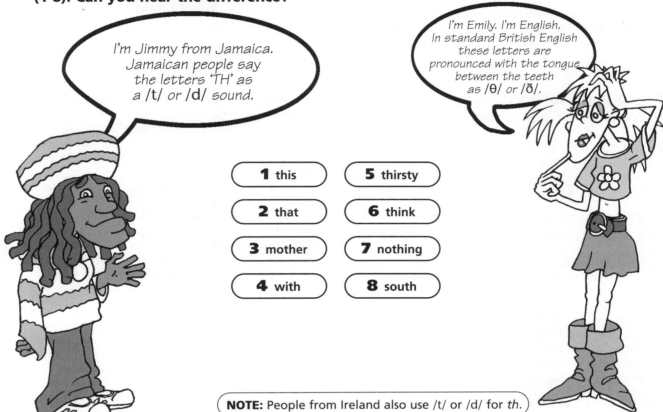

I'm Jimmy from Jamaica. Jamaican people say the letters 'TH' as a /t/ or /d/ sound.

I'm Emily. I'm English. In standard British English these letters are pronounced with the tongue between the teeth as /θ/ or /ð/.

1 this	**5** thirsty
2 that	**6** think
3 mother	**7** nothing
4 with	**8** south

NOTE: People from Ireland also use /t/ or /d/ for *th*.

2 (2/87) **Listen to different people saying these words - once with /d/ or /t/ and once with /ð/ or /θ/. Mark the order you hear the words: 1 = first, 2 = second.**

	/ð/	/d/
1 this	2	1
2 that		
3 mother		
4 with		

	/θ/	/t/
5 thirsty		
6 think		
7 nothing		
8 south		

3 (2/88) **Listen to these sentences. Mark them J (Jamaican) or E (English). Use the pronunciation of *th* in the underlined words to decide.**

1 What's <u>this</u>?   J E

2 <u>That's</u> nice!   J E

3 She's my <u>mother</u>.   J E

4 Who's <u>with</u> you?   J E

5 Are you <u>thirsty</u>?   J E

6 I <u>think</u> you're right.   J E

7 I hope <u>nothing's</u> wrong.   J E

8 I live in the <u>South</u>.   J E

4 **Work in pairs. Take turns to read a sentence from exercise 3 aloud, paying attention to the pronunciation of *th*. Listen and say each time if your partner is using Jamaican or Standard British English pronunciation.**

Answers

Pronunciation Puzzles

1 Letter boxes

3 Mrs Jay: A, H, J, K; **Mr Dee:** B, C, D, E, G, P, T, V, Z (in US English); **Miss Penn:** F, L, M, N, S, X, Z (in UK English); **Mr Hyde:** I, Y; **Mr Coe:** O; **Mrs Fu:** Q, U, W; **Ms Barr:** R

5 1 you, 2 tea, 3 eye, 4 are, 5 Why, 6 queue, 7 Oh, 8 be

2 Web page sorting

2 2 Foster - Oo; 3 Louise - oO; 4 Lestrange - oO

3 1 cartoons - oO; 2 pizzas - Oo; 3 swimming - Oo; 4 dolphin - Oo; 5 thrillers - Oo; 6 lacrosse - oO; 7 Brazil - oO; 8 kebabs - oO; 9 Milan - oO; 10 Poland - Oo; 11 Paris - Oo; 12 giraffe - oO

4 Freddy Foster: 2 Country: Poland; **3** City: Paris; **4** Sport: swimming; **5** Films: thrillers; **6** Animals: dolphins

Louise Lestrange: 1 Fast Food: kebabs; **2** Country: Brazil; **3** City: Milan; **4** Sport: lacrosse; **5** Films: cartoons; **6** Animals: giraffes

5 1 guitars - oO; 2 Walkmans - Oo; 3 cola - Oo; 4 machines - oO; 5 football - Oo; 6 hotels - oO; 7 shampoo - oO; 8 skateboards - Oo; 9 Berlin - oO; 10 Athens - Oo; 11 balloons - oO; 12 sardines - oO
Other things Freddy likes: Walkmans, cola, football, skateboards, Athens
Other things Louise likes: hotels, shampoo, Berlin, balloons, sardines

3 Zoo time

2 2 Vienna - oOo; 3 Montreal - ooO

3 1 koala - oOo; 2 kangaroo - ooO; 3 buffalo - Ooo; 4 octopus - Ooo; 5 flamingo - oOo; 6 polar bear - ooO; 7 antelope - Ooo; 8 elephant - Ooo; 9 chimpanzee - ooO; 10 gorilla - oOo; 11 piranha - oOo; 12 crocodile - Ooo

4 1 Heidelberg: buffalo, octopus, antelope, elephant, crocodile; 2 Vienna: koala, flamingo, gorilla, pirahna; 3 Montreal: kangaroo, polar bear, chimpanzee

5 1 cinema - Ooo; 2 hamburger - Ooo; 3 magazine - ooO; 4 DVD - ooO; 5 chewing gum - Ooo; 6 basketball - Ooo; 7 spaghetti - oOo; 8 lemonade - ooO; 9 bananas - oOo; 10 margarine - ooO; 11 lollipop - Ooo; 12 rollerblades - Ooo

4 Sound like Tarzan

3 1 balloons; 2 ruler; 3 pencils; 4 tomatoes; 5 cactuses

5 1 unstressed; 2 weak; 3 isn't; 4 can; 5 is

6 1 fossil; 2 potatoes; 3 teacher; 4 cassette; 5 sugar; 6 photograph; 7 doctor; 8 acrobats; 9 circus; 10 banana

5 Different habits

3 2 Mercedes; 3 Mercedes; 4 James; 5 Chris; 6 James; 7 Chris; 8 James; 9 James; 10 James; 11 Mercedes; 12 Chris; 13 James; 14 Chris; 15 Mercedes

4 1 drinks /s/; 2 kisses /ɪz/; 3 lives /z/; 4 sends /z/; 5 watches /ɪz/; 6 writes /s/

Pronunciation rule for -s/-es 3rd person singular, Present Simple verb endings
When the final sound of the infinitive verb is one of the 'hissing' sounds - /s/, /z/, /ʃ/, /tʃ/, /dʒ/ or /ʒ/ - we pronounce the -s/-es ending /ɪz/ e.g. kisses, revises, washes, catches, judges, etc.
When the final sound of the infinitive verb is another voiceless consonant sound - /p/, /t/, /k/, /f/, /θ/ - we pronounce the -s/-es ending /s/ e.g. sleeps, eats, wakes, laughs, etc.
When the final sound of the infinitive verb is another voiced consonant - /b/, /d/, /g/, /v/, /ð/, /m/, /n/, /l/, /r/ - or a vowel sound, we pronounce the -s/-es ending /z/ e.g. robs, reads, hugs, loves, brings, swims, phones, sells; draws, enjoys, goes, plays, etc.

6 The picnic

3 1 The Potts family's basket: cups, forks, handkerchiefs, plates
2 The Deeds family's basket: bowls, eggs, herbs, knives, salads, spoons, tomatoes
3 The Aziz family's basket: cheeses, dishes, juices, sandwiches, sausages

4 The Deeds family is taking the most (7 things).
The Potts family is taking the fewest (4 things).

5 1 boxes /ɪz/; 2 brushes /ɪz/; 3 buses /ɪz/; 4 cats /s/; 5 cards /z/; 6 dogs /z/; 7 gloves /z/; 8 oranges /ɪz/; 9 pubs /z/; 10 sandals /z/; 11 scarves /z/; 12 shirts /s/; 13 shoes /z/; 14 watches /ɪz/

Pronunciation rule for -s/-es noun plurals
When the final sound of the singular noun is one of the 'hissing' sounds - /s/, /z/, /ʃ/, /ʒ/, /tʃ/ or /dʒ/ - we pronounce the -s/-es ending /ɪz/ e.g. juices, roses, brushes, sandwiches, sausages, etc.
When the final sound of the singular noun is another voiceless consonant sound - /p/, /t/, /k/, /f/, /θ/ - we pronounce the -s/-es ending /s/ e.g. cups, plates, forks, handkerchiefs, etc.
When the final sound of the singular is another voiced consonant sound - /b/, /d/, /g/, /v/, /ð/, /m/, /n/, /l/, /r/ - or a vowel sound, we pronounce the -s/-es ending /z/ e.g. herbs, cards, eggs, knives, plums, spoons, bowls; tomatoes, shoes, pears, etc.

7 What did they do?

3 2 Astrid; 3 Bud; 4 Pat; 5 Pat; 6 Bud; 7 Astrid; 8 Bud; 9 Astrid; 10 Pat; 11 Bud; 12 Astrid; 13 Bud; 14 Astrid; 15 Pat

4 2 arranged /d/; 3 invited /ɪd/; 4 mended /ɪd/; 5 organised /d/; 6 stopped /t/

Pronunciation rule for -d/-ed regular Past Simple verb endings
When the final sound of the infinitive verb is /t/ or /d/ - we pronounce the -d/-ed ending /ɪd/ e.g. painted, decided, etc.
When the final sound of the infinitive verb is a voiceless consonant sound other than /t/ - /p/, /k/, /f/, /s/, /θ/, /ʃ/, /tʃ/ - we pronounce the -d/-ed ending /t/ e.g. stopped, cooked, laughed, kissed, washed, watched, etc.
When the final sound of the infinitive verb is a voiced consonant sound other than /d/ - /b/, /g/, /v/, /z/, /ð/, /ʒ/, /dʒ/, /m/, /n/, /l/, /r/ - or a vowel sound, we pronounce the -d/-ed ending /d/ e.g. robbed, hugged, loved, organised, loathed, arranged, climbed, phoned, travelled; enjoyed, played, etc.

8 How did they feel?

2 1 surprised /d/; **2** shocked /t/; **3** disgusted /ɪd/;
4 embarrassed /t/; **5** depressed /t/; **6** disappointed /ɪd/;
7 annoyed /d/; **8** frightened /d/; **9** bored /d/; **10** excited /ɪd/

5 3 Rod was bored when his mother took him shopping.
5 Pete was embarrassed when his mother kissed him.
6 David was disgusted when he found a worm in the apple he was eating.
9 Rod was frightened when he was in the house alone one night.
10 David was excited when he went on holiday to America.

6 1 /t/ stressed, relaxed; **2** /d/ confused, scared, amazed, worried; **3** /ɪd/ exhausted, interested

Pronunciation rule for -d/-ed adjective endings
When the final sound of the infinitive verb is /t/ or /d/ - we pronounce the -d/-ed adjective ending /ɪd/ e.g. excited, disgusted, etc.
When the final sound of the infinitive verb is a voiceless consonant sound other than /t/ - /p/, /k/, /f/, /s/, /θ/, /ʃ/, /tʃ/ - we pronounce the -d/-ed adjective ending /t/ e.g. shocked, embarassed, etc.
Note: There are some exceptions to this rule, where the -ed adjective ending is pronounced /ɪd/ - e.g. crooked, naked, wicked.
When the final sound of the infinitive verb is a voiced consonant sound other than /d/ - /b/, /g/, /v/, /z/, /ð/, /ʒ/, /dʒ/, /m/, /n/, /l/, /r/ - or a vowel sound, we pronounce the -d/-ed adjective ending /d/ e.g. surprised, frightened and annoyed, bored, scared, worried, etc.
Note: There are some exceptions to this rule, where the -ed adjective ending is pronounced /ɪd/ - e.g. aged, beloved, jagged, ragged, rugged.

9 Time for a rhyme

2 2 cry - 1; **3** cheese - 5; **4** more - 6; **5** flower - 2; **6** ache - 4

3 2 shower, hour, flower; **3** new shoe, two; **4** break, make, ache; **5** cheese, keys, please; **6** four, more, door

10 Sound-alike pairs

2 2 a two, b too; **3** a hear, b here; **4** a see, b sea;
5 a your, b you're; **6** a Where's, b wears

3 2 eye; **3** read; **4** write; **5** its; **6** know; **7** their; **8** new

5 2 red; **3** I; **4** right; **5** It's; **6** No; **7** knew; **8** There

11 Magic letters e and i

2 Rule 1 is correct.

3 1 angry S; **2** big S; **3** bottle S; **4** computer A; **5** home A;
6 letter S; **7** make A; **8** sun S; **9** these A; **10** time A

5 2 swimming; **3** shopping; **4** forgetting; **5** clapping;
6 sadder; **7** hottest; **8** slimmer; **9** runner; **10** traveller

12 Silent letter clover

2 There are 6 lucky clover leaves (B, W, K, U, T and I). H and L are not lucky clovers. The h in hello is not silent and the l in shoulder is not silent.

4 2 He knew she was ~~k~~nitting when he took his ~~k~~nife and ~~k~~nocked on the door. **3** Who can ~~w~~rite the ~~w~~hole answer? **4** To be ~~h~~onest, I've never seen a g~~h~~ost eat spag~~h~~etti. **5** I g~~u~~ess I left my g~~u~~itar and my bisc~~u~~its in the b~~u~~ilding. **6** Listen! Someone's whis~~t~~ling a Chris~~t~~mas carol in the cas~~t~~le. **7** I wore a su~~i~~t to see my fr~~i~~end in the fru~~i~~t bus~~i~~ness.

5 1 d; **2** c; **3** a; **4** e; **5** b

7 Other words with silent letters: silent b: plumber, climb; silent g: designer; silent gh: daughter, right, bought; silent h: yoghurt; silent n: column; silent o: leopard; silent p: psychologist, pneumatic; silent t: fasten; silent u: guest; silent w: wrist, wrong, two

2 Fun With Phonetics

1 Clothes words

4 /iː/ cheap, sleep; /ɜː/ word, third, learn; /ɑː/ car, banana; /ɔː/ call, door; /uː/ soon, true, you

7 2 bird; **3** hard; **4** bead; **5** fur; **6** four; **7** far; **8** he; **9** who; **10** heard; **11** two; **12** tea

2 Food words

4 1 /æ/ bank; **2** /e/ bread, many; **3** /ɪ/ ticket;
4 /ə/ again, dinner; **5** /ʌ/ cup, wonderful, young;
6 /ɒ/ want; **7** /ʊ/ foot, could

6 2 bell; **3** better; **4** butter; **5** foot; **6** fat; **7** head; **8** had;
9 hot; **10** hit; **11** not; **12** nut

3 Sheep or ship?

4 1 sheep; **2** pull; **3** hut; **4** sports; **5** hers; **6** bins; **7** Luke;
8 barns; **9** pots; **10** an

5 1 pitch; **2** fool; **3** cut; **4** port; **5** earn

4 Sports sounds

4 **1** /k/ key, back, chemist; **2** /h/ hello, behind; **3** /p/ shopping; **4** /f/ phone, coffee; **5** /s/ cinema, Miss; **6** /t/ time, better

5 Job sounds

5 **1** /b/ rubber, club; **2** /d/ saddest, bad; **3** /g/ egg; **4** /v/ clever; **5** /z/ busy; **6** /l/ football, colour; **7** /r/ carry; **8** /w/ one, water; **9** /m/ swimmer, make; **10** /n/ runner

6 Cab or cap?

4 **1** back; **2** cab; **3** bet; **4** live; **5** Zoo; **6** goat; **7** pears; **8** drain; **9** fan; **10** price

5 **1** pear; **2** drain; **3** guard; **4** fan; **5** rise

7 Phonetic hang-gliding

5 **1** /ɔɪ/; **2** /aʊ/; **3** /eə/; **4** /ʊə/; **5** /ɪə/; **6** /əʊ/; **7** /aɪ/; **8** /aʊ/

8 A fancy dress party

3 **1** /eɪ/ break, train, day, eight; **2** /aɪ/ cry; **3** /ɔɪ/ toilet; **4** /əʊ/ boat, yellow; **5** /aʊ/ out; **6** /eə/ careful, bear, their; **7** /ɪə/ ear, here; **8** /ʊə/ poor

4 **2** now; **3** near; **4** buy; **5** beer; **6** boy; **7** toy; **8** tour; **9** toe; **10** pay; **11** poor; **12** pear

9 Phonos the alien

1 **1** The sounds /dʒ/ /ʒ/ /ð/ /ŋ/ and /j/ (on the left) are voiced; **2** The sounds /tʃ/ /ʃ/ and /θ/ (on the right) are voiceless.

4 **2** sheep; **3** jeep; **4** jet; **5** yet; **6** garage; **7** yacht; **8** shot; **9** thing; **10** thin; **11** watch; **12** wash; **13** with; **14** wing; **15** that; **16** chat

10 Sam the spy

1 **2** Poland; **3** Austria; **4** Australia; **5** Germany; **6** France; **7** Greece; **8** Italy; **9** Turkey; **10** Hungary; **11** Argentina; **12** Brazil

3 **1** Sam the spy is twenty years old. **2** He comes from Australia. **3** He lives in a house in Sydney. **4** He's thin and he's got red hair. **5** He enjoys watching television, playing cards and reading books. **6** He loves drinking juice. **7** He's very poor. **8** He likes eating fish. **9** He's got a girlfriend. **10** Her name's Sandra the spy.

4 **2** How old are you? **3** Which languages do you speak? **4** Where exactly do you live? **5** Can you describe yourself? **6** What do you like doing in your free time? **7** What's your favourite food? **8** What's your favourite drink? **9** How much money have you got on you? **10** Have you got a girlfriend or boyfriend?

11 Who killed Sir Benjamin Blue?

3 **2** paper knife; **3** rose garden; **4** rope; **5** hall; **6** sword; **7** nursery; **8** poison; **9** kitchen; **10** pistol; **11** garage; **12** spanner

4 **1** I'm in the room I loved when I was a child. **2** I'm going to drink a nice cup of tea.

5 **1** the nursery; **2** Mrs Turquoise; **3** Poison

12 Furniture and furnishing crossword

2 **2** fireplace; **3** fridge; **4** chairs; **5** desk; **6** cupboard; **7** cooker; **8** sofa; **9** lamp ; **10** carpet; **11** bench; **12** bookshelves; **13** wardrobe; **14** stool; **15** dressing table

3 Across
4 kʌbəd; **5** desk; **7** bʊkʃelvz; **9** kɑːpɪt; **11** bentʃ; **14** dresɪŋ teɪbəl
Down
2 səʊfə; **3** wɔːdrəʊb; **4** kʊkə; **6** tʃeəz; **8** læmp; **10** teɪbəl; **12** frɪdʒ; **13** stuːl

Speak Out

1 Andy the Pronunciation Android

2 **2** h; **3** d; **4** f; **5** c; **6** j; **7** k; **8** l; **9** b; **10** e; **11** m; **12** i; **13** g

2 Shapes dictation

3 **1** teens; **2** chicks; **3** heaps; **4** live; **5** beans; **6** tins; **7** heaps; **8** chicks; **9** hips; **10** bins

3 Sound bingo

2 **2** a shooed, b should; **3** a could, b cooed; **4** a fool, b full; **5** a wooed, b wood; **6** a soot, b suit; **7** a hood, b who'd *(who would)*

4 **1** suit; **2** pool; **3** full; **4** wooed; **5** could; **6** should; **7** who'd

4 Edit the words

3 **1** paper; **2** pen; **3** lane; **4** shed; **5** sailing; **6** men; **7** test; **8** Wait

5 **2** f; **3** c; **4** a; **5** j; **6** g; **7** h; **8** b; **9** i; **10** d

5 Picasso's paints

3 **1** heart; **2** bun; **3** cap; **4** hut; **5** cart; **6** cups

6 Street map dictation

3 **1** a; **2** b; **3** b; **4** a; **5** b; **6** a

7 Find Pharaoh's jewels

3 **1** sun; **2** bang; **3** rank; **4** win; **5** thing; **6** sunk; **7** ban; **8** rang; **9** wing; **10** think

8 Monster maze

3 **1** howl; **2** air; **3** heat; **4** eels; **5** high; **6** heart

5 The Minotaur

9 Get the goblins

3 1 choke; **2** yes; **3** gin; **4** years; **5** Jews

10 Thought bubble dictation

1 1 The underlined sounds in d<u>e</u>n, <u>th</u>en and <u>Z</u>en are voiced.
2 The underlined sounds in <u>t</u>ick, <u>th</u>ick and <u>s</u>ick are voiceless.
3 For the sounds in 2 and 5 you put your tongue between your teeth.
4 For the sounds in 1 and 4 your tongue touches the top of your mouth.
5 For the sounds in 3 and 6 your tongue is curled up in your mouth.

3 1 den; **2** Zen; **3** then; **4** den; **5** thick; **6** tick; **7** sick; **8** tick

Listen In

1 Number fun

1 1 Oo; **2** oO

2 1 90; **2** 18; **3** 4.50; **4** 30; **5** 16; **6** £3.40; **7** 17; **8** 13

4 Oo

6 The number is 4.

2 Can I present you with a present?

1 1 V; **2** N; **3** V; **4** N; **5** V; **6** N; **7** V; **8** N; **9** V; **10** N; **11** V; **12** N

2 1 oO; **2** Oo

4 1 V; **2** N; **3** V; **4** N; **5** N; **6** V

3 Steve Strong and Walter Weak (1)

2 1 weak; **2** strong

5 1 strong, weak; **2** weak, strong; **3** strong, weak; **4** strong, weak; **5** weak, strong; **6** strong, weak; **7** weak, strong; **8** strong, weak

4 Steve Strong and Walter Weak (2)

2 1 strong; **2** weak

6 1 I; **2** C; **3** C; **4** I; **5** I; **6** C; **7** I; **8** C

5 Are you free tonight?

3 1 b; **2** c; **3** a

5 2 She's **go**ing **ska**ting with **Pe**ter this **Sa**tur<u>day</u>.
3 We're **mee**ting <u>at</u> **ni**n<u>e</u> <u>o'</u>cl<u>o</u>ck in fr<u>o</u>nt <u>of</u> th<u>e</u> **cin**<u>e</u>ma.
4 They're **ha**ving <u>a</u> **par**ty <u>at</u> their **hou**s<u>e</u> on **Fri**day.
5 I'm <u>a</u>way on **hol**iday fr<u>o</u>m th<u>e</u> **first** t<u>o</u> th<u>e</u> **fif**teenth <u>of</u> **Au**g<u>u</u>st.

6 The rhythm of the band

1 1 Old Mr **S**and is a **o**ne-man band.
2 You hear him **e**verywhere.
3 Use the **w**ord stress of each **in**strument
4 To match it **w**ith its pair.

2 1 four; **2** three

4

Word stress	instrument 1	instrument 2
O	drum	flute
Oo	cymbals	trumpet
oO	guitar	trombone
Ooo	saxophone	triangle
oOo	maracas	piano
ooO	tambourine	violin
oOoo	accordion	harmonica

7 Internet café

1 1 kasia.popko@**fast**frog.pl
2 theo.prodromou@mailbird.gr
3 helga.kaufmann@surfercat.**at**
4 dieter.**braun**@digimouse.de
5 joelle.dubois@ webchicken.**fr**
6 fabio.fonzo@cyber**dog**.it

8 Tasteless Terry

1 1 b; **2** a; **3** a

2 down; up

4 A: Tasteless Terry's wearing a red shirt. (down intonation over 'shirt')
B: Tasteless Terry's wearing a red shirt, and a green tie. (up intonation over 'shirt', down intonation over 'tie')
C: Tasteless Terry's wearing a red shirt, a green tie and a brown jacket. (up intonation over 'shirt', up intonation over 'tie', down intonation over 'jacket')
D: Tasteless Terry's wearing a red shirt, a green tie, a brown jacket and purple jeans. (up intonation over 'shirt', up intonation over 'tie', up intonation over 'jacket', down intonation over 'jeans')
E: Tasteless Terry's wearing a red shirt, a green tie, a brown jacket, purple jeans and pink trainers. (up intonation over 'shirt', up intonation over 'tie', up intonation over 'jacket', up intonation over 'jeans', down intonation over 'trainers')

9 Job hunting

2 1 up; **2** down

3 1 A: up, B: down; **2** A: down, B: down; **3** B: up, A: up; **4** A: down, B: down; **5** A: up, B: down; **6** A: up, B down; **7** A: down, B: up; **8** A: up, B: down.

10 High Street shopping

2 1 down; **2** up

11 Fred Sure and Rita Unsure

1 1 b; **2** b; **3** b

3 1 a; **2** a; **3** a

4 1 down; **2** up

5 2 F; **3** R; **4** R; **5** F; **6** F; **7** F; **8** R

12 Polite Polly and Rude Rupert

2 **1** a Yes, probably.; **2** b No, probably not.

3 **1** polite and pleasant; **2** rude and angry

4 **2** P; **3** P; **4** R; **5** R; **6** P; **7** P; **8** R

Linking and Accents

1 DVD Collections

2 **1** The Lord_of the Rings
2 Twenty Thousand Leagues_under the Sea
3 Gangs_of New York
4 Charley's_Angels
5 Artificial_Intelligence
6 Wyatt_Earp

4 **1** The Lost World
2 Around the World in Eighty Days
3 Dr Jekyll and Mr Hyde
4 The Secret Garden
5 David Copperfield
6 The Last Samurai

6 **1** The /j/ Elephant Man
2 Catch Me /j/ If You Can
3 Much Ado /w/ About Nothing
4 Charlie /j/ and the Chocolate Factory
5 The /j/ Invisible Man
6 Mickey Blue /w/ Eyes

2 Have we run out of petrol?

1 **2** postponed; **3** like and agree with; **4** arrived unexpectedly;
5 found; **6** enters

2 **1** b; **2** a; **3** e; **4** c; **5** f; **6** d

3 **1** Have we run_out_of petrol?
2 You've put_off the wedding_again!
3 They get_on with_each_other very well.
4 She turned_up_at four_o'clock_in the morning.
5 I came_across_it_in_a jumble sale.
6 He goes_in for_every competition.

4 **2** rejected; **3** cancelled; **4** extinguished; **5** experienced;
6 invented

5 **1** The number of students in each class went down last term.
2 She turned down Andy's invitation.
3 They called the concert off.
4 The firemen put the fire out!
5 We went through some bad times last December!
6 He made the whole thing up.

6 **1** rise; **2** disappear; **3** met (by chance); **4** escaping; **5** enter;
6 continue

7 **1** Prices go /w/ up all the time.
2 I go /w/ away to the country /j/ every weekend.
3 I ran into my /j/ uncle at the party.

4 Look! That boy /j/ on the motorbike's getting away!
5 I wouldn't go /w/ into the /j/ old library /j/ at night!
6 Go /w/ on trying and you'll do /w/ it in the /j/ end.

3 Fred Formal and Ian Informal

1 **1** I would; **2** I am; **3** I have; **4** cannot; **5** It is

2 **1** I'd; **2** I'm; **3** I've; **4** don't; **5** It's

3 **1** You shouldn't smoke.
2 There's a zoo near our town.
3 It'll be ready tomorrow.
4 I didn't like it.
5 Who's that?
6 Don't worry.
7 They'd met years ago.
8 You mustn't panic.
9 Who'd like ice cream?
10 She hasn't arrived yet.

4 How many syllables?

2 **1** uncomf(or)table - 4; **2** cam(e)ra - 2; **3** med(i)cine - 2;
4 hist(o)ry - 2; **5** mis(e)rable - 3; **6** myst(e)ry - 2;
7 rest(au)rant - 2; **8** document(a)ry - 4;
9 math(e)matical - 4; **10** lit(e)rature - 3

4 **2** B; **3** A; **4** B; **5** B; **6** A; **7** B; **8** B; **9** A; **10** A

5 Are you bored?

2 **1** 2, 1; **2** 2, 1; **3** 1, 2; **4** 2, 1; **5** 1, 2; **6** 1, 2

3 **2** B; **3** A; **4** B; **5** B; **6** A; **7** B; **8** B; **9** A; **10** A

6 I'm Australian?

2 **1** I'm Alec. (up arrow)
2 I'm Australian. (up arrow)
3 I'm from Sydney. (up arrow)
4 I'm Belinda. (down arrow)
5 I'm British. (down arrow)
6 I'm from London. (down arrow)

3 **1** Rising (Australian); **2** Falling (British);
3 Rising (Australian); **4** Falling (British);
5 Falling (British); **6** Rising (Australian);
7 Rising (Australian); **8** Falling (British)

5 **1** Statement; **2** Question; **3** Statement; **4** Question;
5 Statement; **6** Statement; **7** Question; **8** Question

7 'Elp me 'Arry

2 **2** 1, 2; **3** 1, 2; **4** 1, 2; **5** 2, 1; **6** 2, 1; **7** 1, 2; **8** 2, 1

3 **2** SB; **3** SB; **4** C; **5** SB; **6** C; **7** C; **8** SB

8 What's dis?

2 **2** 1, 2; **3** 1, 2; **4** 2, 1; **5** 1, 2; **6** 2, 1; **7** 2, 1; **8** 1,2

3 **2** J; **3** E; **4** E; **5** J; **6** E; **7** J; **8** E